# introduction to
# analog computation

# introduction to
# analog computation

**joseph j. blum**
united states air force academy

**harcourt, brace & world, inc.**
new york / chicago / san francisco / atlanta

Library of Congress Catalog Card Number: 69-18204
Printed in the United States of America

# preface

This book is an introduction to computation by means of an analog computer. Since utilization of the computer is the goal of this book, it is designed to "get the student on the computer" as rapidly as possible. The basic concepts required to solve differential equations and simulate simple systems are presented, with only a minimum of theory. The book can be used as a text for courses in analog computation or as a supplement for courses on linear system theory. Because it is self-contained, it can also be used as a supplement for any course in science and engineering in which the student needs to solve differential equations or simulate simple systems, and it can be used by practicing engineers and scientists who are not taking a college course.

A knowledge of basic differential equation theory is assumed, along with an acquaintance with introductory Laplace transform techniques. The latter is used in chapter nine, transfer function simulation, and is required for an understanding of several examples and problems. Because the book was developed as a supplement for a linear systems course, some of the examples and problems involve systems concepts. These present no difficulty for students with a good background in basic physics and mathematics.

A special feature of the book is the use of normalized variables for scaling. Experience has shown that this method of magnitude scaling is easy for the beginning student to understand and use. Time scaling is handled from the point of view of scaling the computer, not the equations. Thus, these two techniques of scaling are completely uncoupled; that is, changing one does not affect the other. The interpretation of results is therefore easier, and an adjustment of the scaling parameters, if necessary, is greatly facilitated. Chapters four and six cover scaling techniques.

A one- or two-credit-hour, one-semester or one-quarter course, together with a laboratory program, can easily be constructed around this book. The laboratory portion is critical and, for that reason, ten laboratory exercises of varying complexity are included in appendix C. If analog computation is studied as an adjunct to another course, only the first seven chapters need be covered, with minimum emphasis on chapters two and five. Chapter ten has been included to show another use for the computer and can be omitted with no loss in continuity.

The book contains 29 worked-out examples, 110 problems, and 10 laboratory exercises. Some problems, as already noted, involve concepts from linear systems analysis, and certain others discuss topics not covered in the text. (Problems 8.6, 8.7, and 8.8, involving the use of quarter-square multipliers, are an example of the latter.) Answers to about one half of the problems are included in the back of the book. Complete worked-out solutions for all problems and laboratory exercises are contained in a Solutions Manual.

Appendix A describes the physical features and operation of a typical small desk top computer. The machine described is the TR-20, manufactured by Electronic Associates, Inc. In addition, the Esterline Angus Speed-Servo strip recorder is described briefly. The text itself is general and can be used with any machine. The only exception is where a "10-volt" machine is assumed.

Grateful acknowledgment is made to Professor Roland E. Thomas, Head of the Department of Electrical Engineering, United States Air Force Academy, and Associate Professor Everette T. Garrett for their reviews of parts of the manuscript. Acknowledgment is also made to other members of the department for the use of some problems and exercises, and for their helpful reviews and comments. Special thanks go to Professor Walter J. Karplus, University of California at Los Angeles, and Professor Roger C. Wood, University of California at Santa Barbara, for their reviews of the entire manuscript and their constructive suggestions. Any shortcomings of this book occurred over their objection rather than through their oversight.

Joseph J. Blum

# contents

# introduction to
# analog computation

# chapter one

**1.0
general
introduction**
Students of science and engineering should have a working knowledge of the use made of modern analog computers in system design and analysis. The programming and determination of the use of an analog computer, in itself, often yields a great deal of insight into a physical system. The analog computer greatly assists the serious student in better understanding various physical phenomena. Both analog and digital computers are of primary value in solving those engineering and scientific problems that are not easily amenable to a classical analytic "pencil and paper" approach. A thorough understanding of computer techniques as applied to linear, constant-coefficient, first- and second-order differential equations describing simple physical systems permits a gradual progression into computer techniques applied to nonlinear and/or nonconstant-coefficient differential equations that more realistically describe actual physical systems. This text serves as an introduction to analog computer methods and is thus addressed primarily to the study of simple linear equations that could describe electrical, mechanical, fluid, thermal, or other relatively simple physical systems. Mastery of the basic application of computational fundamentals serves as an excellent foundation for the use of more sophisticated techniques.

One of the first questions that arises in an introduction to any subject is an understanding of the words by which the subject is named. *Analog* implies that

# introduction

there exists "something" at every instant of time that is to be analogous to the dependent variable (such as displacement, charge, heat, or fluid flow rate) of the physical system. In the analog computer, this analogous "something" is a voltage. For every variable in the given problem there exists a continuous computer voltage that precisely corresponds to every variable. Hence, by continuously measuring and recording these computer voltages, we have a record of the time-varying variables. This record usually takes the form of a graphical representation of a variable versus time.

There are three general classes of output, or readout, devices available for use with most analog computers. These are panel voltmeters (either standard or digital type), cathode ray oscilloscopes, and recorders. The recorders may be single- or multi-channel strip-chart type or they may be $X$-$Y$ type. Large general purpose computers usually have all three types of output devices. Small desk top computers, such as the one described in Appendix A, may have only one type of output device available. The terminals of the various output equipment are usually located on the computer wiring panel, so that the recorder, oscilloscope, or voltmeter can easily be connected to the output of any computing amplifier.

Most readers are probably somewhat familiar with the general characteristics of modern analog, digital, and hybrid computers. The analog computer relies upon the continuous, analogous relationships between the problem variables and the associated computer voltages. The digital computer operates with discrete numerical computations. This concept of *continuous* versus *discrete* problem variables is the basic difference between these two machines. The important point to be made is that each machine has certain advantages and disadvantages depending upon the particular problem at hand. The hybrid computer, which is a combination of both analog and digital computing elements, grew out of the need for combining the unique capabilities of each machine. For example, in a complex engineering design problem involving higher-order, nonlinear differential equations, the analog computer can solve the equations themselves much faster than a digital computer, but the optimization of system parameters can be most easily accomplished by a digital computer that is able to compare the results of an iterative series of solutions with a desired result. The parameters of the system can thus be established to a high degree of accuracy.

In any realistic engineering problem involving the use of the analog computer, it is necessary to scale properly the problem variables so that the voltages that represent the variable use, but do not exceed, the full dynamic range of the computing amplifiers in the machine. In general, both magnitude scaling and time scaling are required. We will discuss these techniques and their applications in detail in Chapters 4 and 6. The point we wish to make here is that the requirement for magnitude and time scaling is obvious if we consider, for example, a space-flight problem, where variables representing distances may be of the order of hundreds of thousands of miles and time may be measured in days. Clearly, such a problem must be scaled so as to reduce all variables to reasonable magnitudes and to yield a solution in, say, a hundred seconds or less. It is usually desirable to obtain solutions in as short a time as possible because computer time is so expensive. It is also inconvenient and time consuming to have to wait long time periods to obtain solutions. We will discuss the technique of magnitude scaling using so-called *normalized variables* and will show how to time scale the *computer*, rather than the *equations*. There are several methods of scaling, some of which, because of their introduction in the early days of analog computation, have found widespread application. Many programmers believe, however, that the use of normalized variables in magnitude scaling is a great deal quicker and easier for a beginning student to master and allows him to progress much sooner to actual computer operation. Further, this technique affords a good deal more insight into the actual problem.

In later chapters we will discuss fundamental analog computer elements and will show how these elements are interconnected to solve typical engineering equations. Solutions to problems are obtained on an analog computer with an interconnected system of computing elements, for example, the summing, inverting, and integrating amplifiers, and potentiometers. More complex problems may require the use of nonlinear components, such as multipliers and diode function generators. The detailed arrangement of these devices is called an analog computer program. The development of such a program will be explained in Chapter 3. We will also discuss the various components (systems) shown in Table 1.1 Basic Analog Computer Organization in Chapter 2 and later chapters.

**Table 1.1**   *Basic Analog Computer Organization*

I   Linear computing elements
        Potentiometers
        Summing amplifiers
        Integrating amplifiers
        Inverting amplifiers

II   Supporting systems
        Mode control system
        Interconnection system
        Output selection and measurement system
        Trouble warning (overload) system

III   Readout systems
        Panel voltmeters
        Cathode ray oscilloscopes
        Strip-chart recorder
        $X$-$Y$ recorder

Finally, it should be noted that this text is an introduction to analog *computation*, not to analog *computers*. Although there is some detailed discussion of the linear computing elements in terms of their electrical characteristics this detail is included in order to give the student a basic understanding of the computer so that he can better utilize it in solving various problems. It should also be noted that the computer does not solve problems; the analyst simply uses it as a tool to assist him in his problem solving. This introduction to analog computation will hopefully allow the student to gain a working knowledge of this very useful tool.

## PROBLEMS

1.1. List, or show diagrammatically, the principal components of a general purpose, analog computing system. Consult one or more of the references at the back of this book. If your school has an analog computing laboratory, check to see what equipment is available.

1.2. Repeat Problem 1.1 for a general purpose, digital computing system.

1.3. Analog and digital computers can be interconnected to form what is called a hybrid computing system. In general, both machines must be specially designed for this capability, and special interface equipment is needed. Show diagrammatically the principal components of a hybrid computing system.

1.4. The "lineage" of modern computers can be traced back through many different devices and machines which, because of their basic continuous or discrete nature, can be described as being analog or digital devices. List some of these devices and categorize them as either analog or digital.

1.5. The use of the analog computer in obtaining solutions to problems in science and engineering is usually only one step in the complete problem-solving process. Draw a block-diagram representation of the problem-solving "system," including the use of the computer in the system. Identify any feedback loops you believe exist. Illustrate with an example.

1.6. State the order and degree of the following differential equations. (*Note:* in this and following problems $t$ means time and the dot notation denotes differentiation with respect to time.)

(a) $y = x\dfrac{dy}{dx} + y\left(\dfrac{dy}{dx}\right)^2$

(b) $\left(\dfrac{d^2y}{dx^2}\right)^2 + x^3\left(\dfrac{dy}{dx}\right)^3 = y$

(c) $\ddot{y} + 2\zeta\omega_n\dot{y} + \omega_n^2 y = f(t)$

(d) $\sqrt{t\dot{y} + at} = b\dot{y}$

1.7. Classify the following differential equations as to linearity, homogeneity, and constancy of coefficients.

(a) $\dot{x} + 2t^2 x = x^2$

(b) $\dot{x} + tx - t^2 = 0$

(c) $a^3\dot{x} + b^2 x = ax$

(d) $x\dot{x} + tx = x\cos\omega t$

1.8. The following differential equation, with the initial condition as shown, describes a physical system:

$$\dot{x} + 0.2x = 0 \qquad \text{with } x(0) = 3$$

Write the solution to this equation. Identify the initial and final values, the independent and dependent variables, and the time constant.

1.9. Given the following differential equation:

$$1.5\ddot{x} + 9\dot{x} + 13.5x = 0$$

Find the natural frequency $\omega_n$ and the damping ratio $\zeta$. Is the system described by this equation underdamped, overdamped, or critically-damped?

1.10. What is the magnitude of the response in Problem 1.8 after a period of time equal to four time constants has passed? After three, two, and one time constants?

# chapter two

Let us first consider the elements or devices which, when properly interconnected on the computer, allow the programmer to solve a problem. To solve
typical linear differential equations, we must be able to add and subtract
variables, change algebraic signs, multiply variables by constants, and integrate. To solve more sophisticated types of problems modern computers also
include devices such as multipliers, diodes, and variable diode function generators. Since we are only considering linear, constant-coefficient systems of
equations, we do not need to discuss such devices. We can perform the mathematical operations listed above in computer problem solving by using devices
called potentiometers, summers, and integrators. The simplest of these, the
potentiometer, is used to multiply a problem variable by a positive constant
less than unity. Its operation is described in the following section. The suc-
ceeding sections deal with the other devices—the direct coupled amplifier, the
operational amplifier, the coefficient, inverting, and summing amplifiers, and
the integrating amplifier.

At this point it should be noted that provisions for differentiation are
usually not provided in a computer because of the problems associated with
mechanizing this mathematical operation. Severe noise problems usually arise,
although these can be overcome. We will see, in our discussion of programming

# linear computing elements

(Chapter 3), that we always express our equations in terms of successive orders of differentiation so the dependent variable and its various derivatives (perhaps displacement, velocity, and acceleration) can be obtained by successive integration.

The potentiometers used in a computer are precision, multi-turn, carbon or wirewound, voltage-divider devices very similar in appearance and function to the common volume control used on a radio or television set. Because they are used to multiply a quantity by a constant less than unity, they are sometimes referred to as attenuators. However, we use the common name *pot*. Chapter 3, "Introduction to Programming," will show how pots are used in wiring ("patching") computer programs. For instance, in a simple magnitude-scaled, first-order equation of the form

$$\dot{x} + 0.900x = 0.800u_{-1}(t)$$

we would require two pots, set to values of 0.900 and 0.800, respectively. The symbol $u_{-1}(t)$ denotes the unit step function (see Problem 3.4).

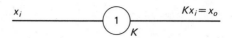

**Figure 2.1**  *Flow diagram symbol for potentiometer*

The flow diagram symbol for the potentiometer is shown in Figure 2.1. The pot setting $K$ is a number between $0^+$ and $1^-$ (pots cannot in general be set to exactly 0 or 1.000 because of their physical construction). Each pot is numbered on the computer patch panel for convenience in wiring and this pot number is entered in the circle on the flow diagram. The value of $K$ is calculated to four decimal places. At least three significant figures are always used on the flow diagram. A portion of the flow diagram for the simple equation above would be as shown in Figure 2.2, assuming we used pot number 3 on the computer patch panel.

**Figure 2.2**

The inputs to pots come from the output of computing amplifiers or from the computer reference supply system. The output (wiper arm) of a pot is usually connected to an amplifier input. As indicated in Figure 2.3, a pot is a three-terminal device. The "top" or "high" end is the input, the output is the sliding contact, and the "bottom" or "low" end is usually grounded. The actual wiring is discussed in Section A.3 (of Appendix A). Since, for most applications, the pot output is connected to an amplifier input, we should examine the electrical loading effect that this has on the pot setting.

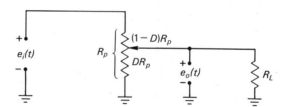

**Figure 2.3**  *Potentiometer loading schematic; $R_L$ is usually an amplifier input resistor*

The output voltage of the potentiometer is delivered to other computing devices, usually amplifiers, which represent finite impedances. The usual situation is as shown in Figure 2.3, where $e_i(t)$ and $e_o(t)$ represent the input and output voltages, respectively; $R_p$ is the total end-to-end resistance of the pot; $D$ represents the *unloaded electrical pot setting*, that is, the pot setting in the absence of any pot load $R_L$; the product $DR_p$ is therefore the resistance between the arm (wiper, or sliding contact) of the pot and the grounded (low) end; and the resistance between the pot input (high) end and the arm is then $(1 - D)R_p$. If the output voltage $e_o(t)$ is delivered to an open circuit ($R_L$ infinite), then the relationship between output and input is, by voltage division,

$$e_o(t) = e_i(t) \left[ \frac{DR_p}{DR_p + (1 - D)R_p} \right] = De_i(t) \qquad (2.1)$$

In the presence of pot loading ($R_L$ finite), this simple relation (2.1) no longer holds because $e_o(t)$ appears across the parallel combination of $DR_p$ and $R_L$. We then have

$$e_o(t) = e_i(t) \left[ \frac{DR_pR_L/(DR_p + R_L)}{DR_pR_L/(DR_p + R_L) + (1 - D)R_p} \right] \quad (2.2)$$

which reduces to

$$e_o(t) = e_i(t) \left[ \frac{1}{1/D + (1 - D)R_p/R_L} \right] \quad (2.3)$$

If we define the bracketed term to represent the *true (effective) pot setting K*, we then have

$$e_o(t) = Ke_i(t) \quad (2.4)$$

where

$$K \triangleq \frac{1}{1/D + (1 - D)R_p/R_L} \quad (2.5)$$

We see from this result that the true pot setting $K$ (which is the value to which we must set the pot) depends on the value of $R_L$, or the resistance to which the pot is connected. Since connecting a pot into different amplifier input "gains" corresponds to loading it with different resistances $R_L$, we conclude that

(1)  pots must be set to their desired value *under load*,
(2)  changing this load changes the setting.

To see the effect of pot loading, consider the following example.


*example 2.1*

Suppose a pot is set to the value of 0.100 under a *no load* (infinite $R_L$) condition. This means that the unloaded electrical pot setting $D$ is 0.100. We should be able, based on the above results to predict the true (effective) pot setting $K$, which results when the pot is connected to different amplifier input gains (different values of $R_L$). On some 10-V computers, "gain 1" on an amplifier corresponds to an $R_L$ of 100 k$\Omega$, and "gain 10" means we are connected to an $R_L$ of 10 k$\Omega$. The actual value for $R_p$ of this pot is about 5900 $\Omega$. Hence, if $D$ is 0.100 and the output is connected to gain 10 of an amplifier, we have from (2.5)

$$K = \frac{1}{1/0.1 + (0.9)5.9/10} = \frac{1}{10.53} = 0.0949$$

Thus, we see that changing the value of pot loading would introduce a significant error (over 5%) into the problem.


The conclusion to be drawn from Example 2.1 is, as stated earlier, that *all pots used in a given program must be set under load*. Furthermore, if the load is changed the pot *must* be reset. (We discuss the mechanics of actually setting the pots in Appendix A, "Computer Operation.")

**direct coupled amplifier**

In Section 2.0 we discussed the need for having summing and integrating amplifiers in any general purpose analog computer. The dc amplifier, in various network configurations, serves as the heart of these devices. It is a high-gain (typically of the order $\sim 10^8$) voltage amplifier that functions at all frequencies down to and including zero. This gain response differs from that of the usual ac voltage amplifier, as shown in Figure 2.4.

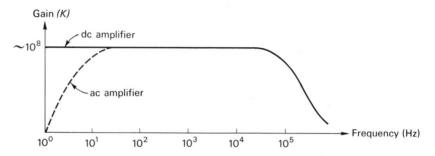

**Figure 2.4**  *Direct coupled amplifier response*

We use a curved-front symbol for the high-gain dc amplifier as shown in Figure 2.5. The reader should note that this symbol differs from the flow diagram symbol used for a summer or integrator (see Section 2.4). The high-gain amplifier is connected in various network configurations to build summing and integrating amplifiers; this is discussed in Section 2.4 and at that time the correct symbolism is introduced. The negative sign associated with the gain $K$ in the high-gain amplifier denotes the fact that this device inverts the signal that passes through it, that is, the output is changed in sign from the input.

**Figure 2.5**  *Symbol for high-gain amplifier*

For purposes of analysis, the high-gain amplifier is assumed to have an infinite input impedance and a zero output impedance. The input and output voltages are, in general, functions of time and are measured with respect to ground. The output $e_o(t)$ is limited by the amplifier design to the range $\pm 13$ V (at least this is true for so-called "10-V machines," such as some small desk top computers). Since $K$ is of the order of $10^8$, this requires that $e_i(t)$ must remain less than about 0.1 $\mu$V. This results in the input point (the input to the base of the first stage) being called a "virtual ground" because, for proper amplifier operation, this point must remain near zero, or ground, potential. We use this fact in the analysis of the operational amplifier.

12    linear computing elements

The high-gain amplifier that is connected in a network as shown in Figure 2.6 is called an operational amplifier. By considering different values and/or elements for the input resistor $R_i$ and the feedback circuit element, we can build a summing amplifier, an integrating amplifier, etc. Note that the operational amplifier configuration uses the high-gain dc amplifier with associated input and feedback circuitry. The input and output voltages, $e_i(t)$ and $e_o(t)$, are measured with respect to ground.

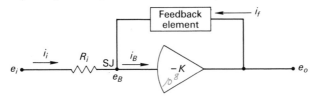

**Figure 2.6** *Operational amplifier*

All the voltages and currents shown in Figure 2.6 are time-varying quantities, but note that the functional dependence (for example, $e_i(t)$, etc.) has been dropped for convenience of notation. We analyze the circuit to establish relationships for the cases where the feedback is either resistive or capacitive. For a resistor in the feedback, we have the coefficient, inverting, and summing amplifiers (Section 2.4). For a capacitor in the feedback, we have a device that performs the mathematical operation of integration, the integrating amplifier (Section 2.5).

We consider first the case where the feedback circuit element in the operational amplifier (Figure 2.6) is a pure resistor $R_f$. From Section 2.2, $e_B$ is essentially zero (virtual ground) and $i_B \approx 0$. We then write the Kirchhoff current law equation at the point marked SJ (summing junction),

$$i_i + i_f = 0 \tag{2.6}$$

and

$$\left(\frac{e_i - e_B}{R_i}\right) + \left(\frac{e_o - e_B}{R_f}\right) = 0 \tag{2.7}$$

From Section 2.2,

$$e_o = -Ke_B \Rightarrow e_B = -\frac{e_o}{K} \tag{2.8}$$

Combining (2.7) and (2.8)

neglect because of $\frac{1}{10^8}$

$$\frac{e_o}{R_f} = -\frac{e_i}{R_i} - \frac{1}{K}\left(\frac{e_o}{R_i} + \frac{e_o}{R_f}\right) \tag{2.9}$$

Since $K \cong 10^8$, the last term in (2.9) is 0 to a very good approximation. We then obtain

$$e_o = -\left(\frac{R_f}{R_i}\right) e_i \tag{2.10}$$

This last relation means that the output of the amplifier is related to the input by a "gain" factor $R_f/R_i$, which can be greater than or equal to unity. For some

10-V computers, $R_f$ is a fixed 100 kΩ precision (0.01% tolerance or better) resistor and $R_i$ is either 100 kΩ or 10 kΩ. The two different values for $R_i$ allow one to select two different gain settings. Using (2.10), we see

$$\frac{R_f}{R_i} = \frac{100 \text{ k}\Omega}{100 \text{ k}\Omega} = 1 \quad \Rightarrow e_o = -e_i \quad \Rightarrow \text{gain 1}$$

$$\frac{R_f}{R_i} = \frac{100 \text{ k}\Omega}{10 \text{ k}\Omega} = 10 \Rightarrow e_o = -10e_i \Rightarrow \text{gain 10}$$

When $R_f \neq R_i$, we have a device commonly called a *coefficient amplifier*. When $R_f = R_i$, the coefficient by which the output is related to the input (namely, the gain) is unity, and thus we have a simple inverting amplifier, or *inverter*. One should not lose sight of the fact, however, that every amplifier inverts the signal; we simply give an amplifier that only changes the sign of the input the special name of inverter.

If the above analysis is extended to the case where we have more than one input (hence more than one $R_i$), we have a device called a summing amplifier or *summer*. Such an arrangement is shown in Figure 2.7. Applying equa-

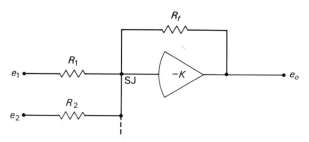

**Figure 2.7**   *Summing amplifier*

tions (2.6) through (2.9) we obtain the relation between the output $e_o$ and the two inputs $e_1$ and $e_2$ to be

$$e_o = - \left( \frac{R_f}{R_1} e_1 + \frac{R_f}{R_2} e_2 \right) \tag{2.11}$$

Obviously, a similar relation is found if more than two inputs are used. In (2.11), if $R_1$ is 100 kΩ and $R_2$ is 10 kΩ, we would have, if $R_f$ is fixed at 100 kΩ,

$$e_o = -(e_1 + 10e_2) \tag{2.12}$$

If any input is negative, we can perform the mathematical operation of subtraction. On a typical small computer, there are usually available two gain 10 and two gain 1 inputs to each summing amplifier. Appendix A on computer operation shows the physical connection of summers and/or inverters.

It is important at this point to introduce the symbolism used on analog computer flow diagrams or flow charts. The complete notation of Figure 2.7 for the summer is too involved for use in normal flow diagramming. Instead, we use for the summer the standardized symbol shown in Figure 2.8. Plastic templates are available for constructing this and other (pot, integrator, etc.) symbols on the flow diagram.

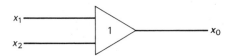

**Figure 2.8** *Flow diagram symbol for the summer*

For the specific data used in Equation (2.12), assuming amplifier number 2 was used for the summer, the correct flow diagram would be as shown in Figure 2.9. Note that the gain 1 associated with input $x_1$ is shown. Normally,

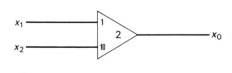

**Figure 2.9**

if only one gain 1 input is used (that is, a simple inverter), it is not necessary to enter the numeral 1 next to the input. In the case of summers though in order to avoid any ambiguity, all input gains can be entered. A summary of flow diagram symbols for all linear computing components discussed in this Chapter is contained in Table 2.1, page 18.

We should also point out here that the relations obtained above, namely,

$$e_o = -e_i \tag{2.13}$$

for the simple inverter and

$$e_o = -(e_1 + e_2 + e_3) \tag{2.14}$$

for a summer with three gain 1 inputs are defining relations in terms of input and output *voltages*. We may wish these voltages to be analogous to variables whose magnitudes are appreciably greater than the design range of the computing amplifiers in most ordinary 10-V computers. This introduces the necessity for magnitude scaling, which will be formally discussed in Chapter 4. We will see there that all amplifier outputs become normalized quantities which are ratios of the actual voltage divided by some "normalizing voltage" $e_N$. This normalizing voltage is a positive quantity equal in magnitude to the computer reference voltage ($+10$ V in the case of common 10-V machines). The ratios $e/e_N$ are then always analogous to the "normalized variables" in our problem. The symbol $x$ is reserved for a normalized variable. Using this concept, (2.13) and (2.14) become

$$\frac{e_o}{e_N} = -\frac{e_i}{e_N} \tag{2.15}$$

and

$$\frac{e_o}{e_N} = -\left(\frac{e_1}{e_N} + \frac{e_2}{e_N} + \frac{e_3}{e_N}\right) \tag{2.16}$$

or

$$x_o = -x_i \tag{2.17}$$

and

$$x_o = -(x_1 + x_2 + x_3) \tag{2.18}$$

Since amplifier outputs should never be allowed to exceed the range $\pm 10$ V and since $e_N = +10$ V, it is clear that the normalized outputs $x_o$ in (2.17) and (2.18) can only vary between $+1$ and $-1$. We do not use the term *voltages* at various points in our computer flow diagram but, rather, we always speak of *normalized quantities*. In fact, the voltmeter on our computer would be more accurately described if called a "ratiometer," since it measures the normalized ratio $e/e_N$.

**2.5**
**integrating amplifier**

As stated in Section 2.3, the operational amplifier of Figure 2.6 functions as an integrating amplifier when the feedback circuit element is a capacitor. As in the coefficient and summing amplifiers, the input resistor $R_i$ has 100 k$\Omega$ or 10 k$\Omega$ resistance. The situation is then as shown in Figure 2.10.

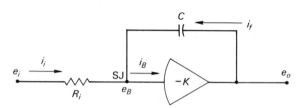

Figure 2.10   *Integrating amplifier*

We repeat the analysis of Section 2.4 and derive a relation between input voltage $e_i$ and output voltage $e_o$. Because $i_B \approx 0$, we again have

$$i_i + i_f = 0 \tag{2.19}$$

$$\left(\frac{e_i - e_B}{R_i}\right) + C\frac{d}{dt}(e_o - e_B) = 0 \tag{2.20}$$

Using (2.8) and rearranging,

$$C\frac{de_o}{dt} = -\frac{e_i}{R_i} - \frac{1}{K}\left(\frac{e_o}{R_i} + C\frac{de_o}{dt}\right) \tag{2.21}$$

This is a relation analogous to (2.9) for the coefficient amplifier, and since $K \cong 10^8$, the last term again may be dropped in comparison with the other two. We then have

$$\frac{de_o}{dt} = -\frac{1}{R_iC}e_i \quad + \; e_o(0) \tag{2.22}$$

~~initial condition on cap.~~

or, in integral form

$$e_o = -\frac{1}{R_iC}\int e_i\, dt \tag{2.23}$$

Thus we have a device which has as an output the integral of a time-varying input $e_i(t)$. Equation (2.23) is the defining *voltage* relation.

As with the amplifiers we have discussed earlier, $R_i$ is either a 100 k$\Omega$ or 10 k$\Omega$ resistor. The feedback capacitor is, in the case of some small desk top computers, a fixed precision 10 μF capacitor. Thus, we again have a gain 1 or gain 10 device. Each integrator can be wired with as many as three gain 1 and two gain 10 inputs. We will show the detailed connections in Section A.4. The symbol shown in Figure 2.11 is used for the integrator in our flow diagrams.

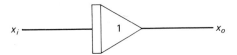

**Figure 2.11**    *Flow diagram symbol for integrator*

Note that we have not as yet included any provision for the proper initial condition (IC) in our integration. We, of course, must have the capability of performing the following type of mathematical operation,

$$e_o(t) = -\left(\frac{1}{R_i C} \int_0^t e_i(t)\, dt - e_o(0)\right) \tag{2.24}$$

where $e_o(0)$ is the initial condition on the time-varying output $e_o(t)$. This operation is accomplished on the computer by patching into the integrator initial-condition network a voltage proportional to the desired IC. This has the effect of charging a capacitor to the correct value, such that the capacitor voltage appears at the output at time $t = 0$. The IC is shown on the integrator symbol used in flow diagrams as shown in Figure 2.12. In usual practice, the voltage $e_o(0)$ comes from computer reference (either $+$ or $-$, depending upon the IC of the problem) and a pot is used, unless the value is exactly $\pm 1.00$. The initial condition input is inverted through the integrator, so the *negative* of the desired IC must be programmed. This is shown in Figure 2.12.

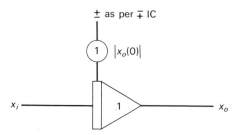

**Figure 2.12**    *Flow diagram symbol for integrator with given initial condition*

We can again derive a normalized relation for the integrator similar to (2.17) and (2.18). From (2.24)

$$\frac{e_o}{e_N} = -\left(\frac{1}{R_i C} \int_0^t \frac{e_i}{e_N}\, dt - \frac{e_o(0)}{e_N}\right) \tag{2.25}$$

or

$$x_o = -\left(\frac{1}{R_i C} \int_0^t x_i\, dt - x_o(0)\right) \tag{2.26}$$

As before, $e_N$ is the normalizing voltage equal to positive computer reference voltage and the ratios $e/e_N$ are normalized quantities whose values lie in the range $+1$ to $-1$. When we discuss magnitude scaling using normalized variables in Chapter 4, we will return to (2.26) and show how $x_o$ and $x_i$ are analogous to normalized problem variables. In other words, if $y$ is our problem variable and $y_N$ is its associated normalizing constant, we use the "bridging relation"

$$\frac{y}{y_N} \triangleq x_y = \frac{e}{e_N} \tag{2.27}$$

to show how the normalized computer amplifier voltage $e/e_N$ is analogous to the normalized problem variable $x_y$.

**2.6
summary**   Table 2.1 shows the symbols used in analog computer flow diagrams for the linear computing elements discussed in this chapter. The inputs and outputs are stated in terms of normalized quantities. No amplifier gains are shown,

Table 2.1   *Flow Diagram Symbols for Linear Computing Elements*

| Linear Computing Element | Symbol | | Mathematical Operation Performed |
| --- | --- | --- | --- |
| | *Input* | *Output* | |
| Potentiometer (pot) | $x_i$ —◯— $K$ | $x_o = K x_i$ | Multiplication by a constant |
| Inverter | $x_i$ —▷— | $x_o = -x_i$ | Sign reversal |
| Summer | $x_1$, $x_2$ —▷— | $x_o = -(x_1 + x_2)$ | Addition |
| Summer | $x_1$, $-x_2$ —▷— | $x_o = -(x_1 - x_2)$ | Subtraction |
| Integrator | $\pm$ as per $\mp$ IC ◯ $|x_o(0)|$ ; $x_i$ —▷— | $-\left(\int_0^t x_i\, dt - x_o(0)\right)$ | Integration |

which implies that all gains are unity ($R_i$, for example, of 100 k$\Omega$). The integrator initial condition is $+x_o(0)$. In a flow diagram composed of these symbols, the number of the device used is always entered inside the symbol.

## PROBLEMS

2.1. Consider an analog computer potentiometer whose resistance $R_p$ is 30 k$\Omega$. Assume the pot output is connected to a 100 k$\Omega$ amplifier input resistor. This means that $R_L$ in Equation (2.5) is 100 k$\Omega$. If the unloaded electrical pot setting $D$ is 0.500, find the true (effective) pot setting $K$.

2.2. Derive Equation (2.11), the relation between the output $e_o$ and the two imputs $e_1$ and $e_2$.

2.3. Show the flow diagram symbol for the device shown in Figure 2.13.

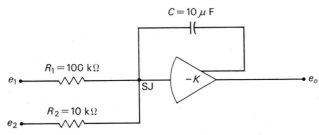

Figure 2.13

2.4. Show that the operational amplifiers shown in Figure 2.14 (a) and (b) could theoretically be used to obtain the derivative with respect to time of the input voltage $e_i$.

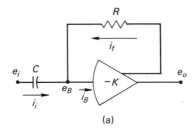

(a)

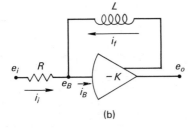

(b)

Figure 2.14

2.5. Based on your understanding of the physical meaning of differentiation, give a reason why the direct application of this operation on the analog computer could cause serious problems. Consider an input signal having an arbitrary waveform.

2.6. Write the expression for the output $x_o$ of each of the combinations of linear computing elements shown in Figure 2.15.

(a)

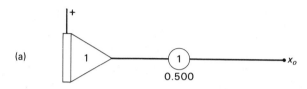

(b)

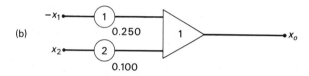

(c)

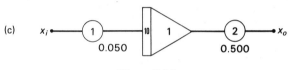

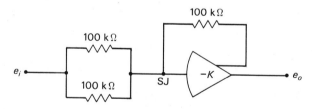

**Figure 2.15**

2.7. Compute the gain of the operational amplifier of Figure 2.16.

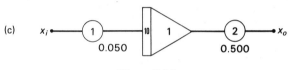

100 kΩ

100 kΩ

$e_i$

100 kΩ

SJ

−K

$e_o$

**Figure 2.16**

2.8. In Section B.1, a new notation is introduced involving the combination of the high-gain amplifier of Figure 2.5 and its associated input circuitry. This is done for convenience of notation in diode circuits. Assuming an input resistor of 10 kΩ and a feedback resistor of 100 kΩ, represent the operational amplifier in the following three ways:

(a) In terms of the complete notation of Figure 2.6.

(b) In terms of the combined notation of Section B.1.

(c) In terms of the usual flow diagram symbol suggested by Figure 2.8.

**20    linear computing elements**

**2.9.** Find the differential equations solved by the two circuits of Figure 2.17.

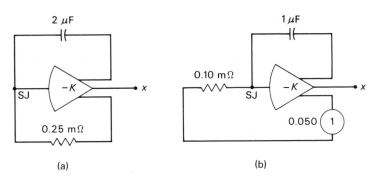

(a)

(b)

**Figure 2.17**

**2.10.** Do some outside reading (in reference 14, Section 2.3 for example), and describe briefly the use of *pot set*, *hold*, and *reset* relays with high-gain amplifiers. A qualitative discussion of these computer modes, for one typical machine, is given in Section A.2.

# chapter three

**3.0 introduction** In this chapter we discuss the details of programming the computer to obtain solutions of standard low-order linear, constant-coefficient differential equations. We consider those equations that are common to the study of mechanical, electrical, thermal, etc. systems. In order not to complicate unduly the discussion at this early point, we do not go through the complete magnitude and time scaling procedures. These techniques will be discussed in Chapters 4 and 6, respectively. This is not to imply that scaling is not needed; in fact, an equation describing any real physical system must almost always be scaled. To enable us to gain a basic understanding of programming techniques, we can simply assume that the constants chosen in the systems we use for examples are such that scaling is not required. In Chapter 2 a special symbol $x$ was introduced to denote a *normalized variable* (that is, the dependent variable in a magnitude-scaled equation). The examples in this chapter are always written in terms of $x$ and its derivatives. The dot notation is used to denote orders of differentiation with respect to time.

The combination of the standard symbols for linear computing elements contained in Table 2.1 is called a flow diagram (or flow chart). A special Analog Computer Worksheet is sometimes useful when one is programming a computer. One possible arrangement of such a worksheet is shown in Figure

# introduction
# to programming

3.1. The flow diagram can be entered on one side of this worksheet and a check procedure called a static check can easily be calculated using this form. We will see an example of its use in Chapter 5. Neatness is very important in preparing analog computer flow diagrams; many errors in computer patching are directly traceable to poorly prepared flow diagrams.

In the following section we discuss the indirect programming method. Direct programming involves the systematic step-by-step operations necessary to obtain some required mathematical function or quantity. Consider, for example, the programming necessary to compute the Hamiltonian integral

$$I = \int_{t_1}^{t_2} (T - V) \, dt \tag{3.1}$$

It would first be necessary to form the generalized kinetic energy $T$, and potential energy $V$ functions, then to take their difference, and, finally, to integrate the resulting expression over the required limits. The computation of the so-called Lagrangian function $T - V$ could involve all the linear computing elements we have considered, along with multipliers, diode function generators, etc. At any rate, the computation of (3.1) would involve direct programming.

For the kinds of equations we must solve we will find the technique of

| Lab _____<br>**ANALOG COMPUTER WORKSHEET** | Name | | |
|---|---|---|---|
| | Date | | Sect. |
| | Course | | Prob. |

| Calculations | STATIC CHECK | | | | | | | |
|---|---|---|---|---|---|---|---|---|
| | Amp. no. | Output vari. | Calc. value | Meas. value | Pot no. | Pot setting | Calc. value | Meas. value |
| | | | | | | | | |
| | | | | | | | | |
| | | | | | | | | |
| | | | | | | | | |
| | | | | | | | | |
| | | | | | | | | |
| | | | | | | | | |
| | | | | | | | | |
| | | | | | | | | |
| | | | | | | | | |
| | | | | | | | | |
| | | | | | | | | |
| | | | | | | | | |
| | | | | | | | | |
| | | | | | | | | |
| | | | | | | | | |
| | | | | | | | | |
| | | | | | | | | |
| | | | | | | | | |
| | | | | | | | | |
| | | | | | | | | |
| | | | | | | | | |
| | | | | | | | | |
| | | | | | | | | |
| | | | | | | | | |

**Magnitude-Scaled Equations and Initial Conditions**

**Notes**

| Run | Plot | F1 | F2 | F3 | Sel. | Arm | Pen | n | Normalizing Constants |
|---|---|---|---|---|---|---|---|---|---|
| | | | | | | | | | |
| | | | | | | | | | |
| | | | | | | | | | |
| | | | | | | | | | |
| | | | | | | | | | |

| From Static Check Sheet | | | From Scaling Calculations | | To be used in Program Check | |
|---|---|---|---|---|---|---|
| Lab _____<br>**PROGRAM CHECK WORKSHEET** | | | **Name** | | | |
| | | | **Date** | | **Sect.** | |
| | | | **Course** | | **Prob.** | |

**PROGRAM CHECK WORKSHEET**

| From Static Check Sheet | | | From Scaling Calculations | | To be used in Program Check | |
|---|---|---|---|---|---|---|
| Amp. no. | Normalized variable symbol | Static check IC value | Normalizing constant symbol | Normalizing constant numerical value | Unscaled variable symbol | Variable's descaled static check value |
| | | | | | | |
| | | | | | | |
| | | | | | | |
| Amp. or pot no. | Programmed forcing function | Static check IC value | Normalization algebraic value | Normalization numerical value | Unscaled forcing function | Forcing function's descaled static check value |
| | | | | | | |
| | | | | | | |
| | | | | | | |
| | | | | | | |

**Unscaled Equation:**
**Substitution of Descaled**
      **static check values:**
**Numerical Reduction:**

**Equation Verification:**

**Unscaled nonzero initial conditions:**
**Substitution of descaled**
      **static check values:**
**Nonzero IC verification:**

**Figure 3.1** *Analog Computer Worksheet and Program Check Worksheet*

indirect programming more useful. This technique is used to solve differential equations whereas, in general, direct programming is used to generate a particular expression, such as the integral (3.1).

To apply the indirect programming method to differential equations, we first divide the equation through by the coefficient of the highest-order term and then we solve for the *negative* of this term. Assuming this quantity is available, we then successively integrate it to obtain all the remaining derivatives, down to and including the zeroth-order term. The terms comprising the highest-order expression are then "fed back" (through appropriate pots set to the coefficient associated with each term) and summed at the summer whose input was originally assumed to be the negative of the highest-order derivative. This procedure can probably best be illustrated by a numerical example.

**3.1
indirect
programming**

### example 3.1

Consider the familiar mass, spring, damper system shown in Figure 3.2. The

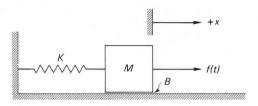

Figure 3.2

numbers in this simple example have been chosen so that no scaling is necessary for a computer solution. Hence, the displacement can be expressed as a normalized variable $x$. We can write the equation of motion as

$$M\ddot{x} + B\dot{x} + Kx = f(t) \tag{3.2}$$

If $f(t)$ is a step function $Fu_{-1}(t)$, we can write (3.2) as

$$-\ddot{x} = \frac{B}{M}\dot{x} + \frac{K}{M}x - \frac{F}{M}u_{-1}(t) \tag{3.3}$$

Then, if our values are given as

$$M = 2.0 \text{ kg}$$
$$B = 0.32 \text{ N-sec/m}$$
$$K = 1.28 \text{ N/m}$$
$$F = 0.6 \text{ N}$$

we may write

$$-\ddot{x} = 0.160\dot{x} + 0.640x - 0.300u_{-1}(t) \tag{3.4}$$

This equation is written in the proper form for indirect programming. Let us further assume that we have initial conditions

$$x(0) = 0$$
$$\dot{x}(0) = -0.3 \text{ m/sec} \tag{3.5}$$

We note, from (3.4), that the damping ratio $\zeta$ is 0.1 and the natural frequency $\omega_n$ is 0.8 rad/sec. We therefore should expect that the response is a lightly-damped sinusoid. Furthermore, the final value is

$$x_f = \frac{F}{M\omega_n^2} = 0.469 \text{ m} \tag{3.6}$$

Now, if we *assume* for the moment that $-\ddot{x}$ is available at the input to a summer (number 1), we can obtain the lower-order terms by successive integration. The *partial* flow diagram is shown in Figure 3.3. Since $-\ddot{x}$, from (3.4),

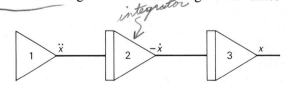

Figure 3.3

is composed of terms involving $+\dot{x}$ and $+x$, multiplied by appropriate positive constants, and $u_{-1}(t)$, we can obviously feed back these terms using the arrangement shown in Figure 3.4. Inverting amplifier number 4 is used to

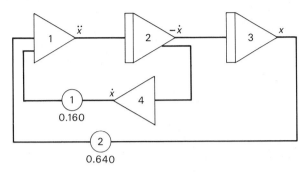

Figure 3.4

obtain $+\dot{x}$. Now, the one remaining term to complete the $-\ddot{x}$ input to amplifier 1 (A1) is $-0.3u_{-1}(t)$. This term is obtained from $-$ computer reference using pot 3. (More will be said about step functions in Section 3.3.) Finally, the IC on $\dot{x}$ is obtained using pot 4. The complete flow diagram for this example is then as shown in Figure 3.5.

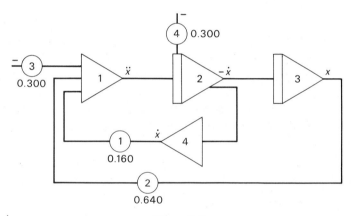

Figure 3.5

The reader should review Figure 3.5 carefully as an aid to understanding the proper notation and layout used in analog computer flow diagrams. Particular note should be made of the handling of the IC. We required $\dot{x}(0) = -0.300$ for the problem, but we had $-\dot{x}$ at the output of A2. Hence, since $-\dot{x}(0) = +0.300$, and since we always have an inversion through an amplifier, we must use an IC on A2 of $-0.300$. This is a very common source of error.

The reader should, if possible, patch and run this example and verify the operation. He should find that $x_{\max}(t) \cong 0.9$ m at $t \cong 4.9$ sec. The observed $x_f \cong 0.471$ m.

The above example was developed in some detail to aid the student in applying the method of indirect programming. The next example requires more work on the part of the reader.

## example 3.2

Consider the simple two-loop electrical network shown in Figure 3.6. Loop currents $i_1(t)$ and $i_2(t)$ may be chosen as shown. All initial conditions are zero, and the switch is closed at time $t = 0$. The values for the elements are

$$R_1 = 2\,\Omega \qquad L_1 = 2.5\,\text{H} \qquad E = 0.75\,\text{V}$$
$$R_2 = 3\,\Omega \qquad L_2 = 5\,\text{H}$$

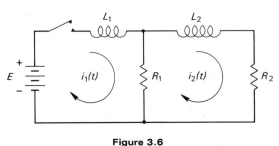

**Figure 3.6**

The Kirchhoff voltage law equations are

$$E u_{-1}(t) = L_1 \frac{di_1}{dt} + R_1(i_1 - i_2) \tag{3.7}$$

$$0 = L_2 \frac{di_2}{dt} + (R_1 + R_2)i_2 - R_1 i_1 \tag{3.8}$$

These may be written in the proper form for indirect programming by solving for the negative of the highest-order derivative. Since, as in Example 3.1, no

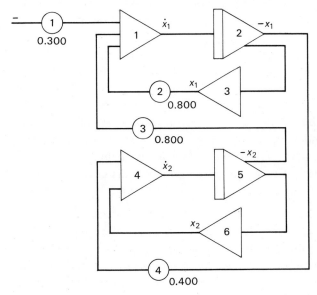

**Figure 3.7**

magnitude scaling is required in this simple problem we may also replace $i_1$ and $i_2$ by the normalized variables $x_1$ and $x_2$. We then have

$$-\dot{x}_1 = \frac{R_1}{L_1} x_1 - \frac{R_1}{L_1} x_2 - \frac{E}{L_1} u_{-1}(t) \tag{3.9}$$

$$-\dot{x}_2 = \left(\frac{R_1 + R_2}{L_2}\right) x_2 - \frac{R_1}{L_2} x_1 \tag{3.10}$$

Using the element values given above, these equations become

$$-\dot{x}_1 = 0.800x_1 - 0.800x_2 - 0.300u_{-1}(t) \tag{3.11}$$
$$-\dot{x}_2 = 1.00x_2 - 0.400x_1 \tag{3.12}$$

The reader should verify that the flow diagram of Figure 3.7 is correct.

Then the reader should verify, both analytically and on the computer, that the expected final (steady state) values of the first-order responses of $i_1(t)$ and $i_2(t)$ to the step input are

$$i_{1_f} = \frac{E}{R_1 R_2/(R_1 + R_2)} = \frac{0.75}{\frac{6}{5}} = 0.625 \text{ A}$$

$$i_{2_f} = \frac{R_1}{R_1 + R_2} i_{1_f} = \frac{2}{5} \cdot \frac{5}{8} = 0.250 \text{ A}$$

To check these on the computer, one must address A3 and A6, respectively, and then, after steady state is reached, read the amplifier outputs using the null comparison method described in Appendix A. We will show the response of $i_1(t)$ versus $t$ in the next section when we discuss the proper labeling of computer-generated strip recorder plots.

In both Examples 3.1 and 3.2, one may note that the negative of the highest-order derivative was assumed to be present at the input to a summer, not an integrator. Although summing can physically be accomplished using an integrator (we have available several gain 1 and gain 10 inputs which could be used), it is generally not a good practice. Usually, accuracy is lessened if one sums on an integrator and, in addition, the highest-order derivative no longer appears explicitly at the output of an amplifier. We may wish to plot, or at least observe, the highest-order term and, furthermore, we will find in Chapter 5 that we must have this term available to complete the program check procedure. Hence, except in certain cases which we will point out, we never sum at the inputs to integrators.

**3.2 labeling of computer plots**

The wiring and operation of one type of recorder is discussed in Section A.5. We note there that the recorder operates at paper feed-rate speeds of 0.75, 1.5, 3, 6, and 12 in./min. We find it very convenient to establish a simple rule for labeling the plot in terms of seconds. Specifically, we simply want a relation, or rule, which gives the elapsed time, in seconds, at the inch marks along the recording. To do this we note the following relation between paper speed (as selected by the control labeled S2, Figure A.5) and time, in seconds, at the first inch mark on the plot.

| *Paper speed* | *Time at* 1 in. *mark* |
|---|---|
| 0.75 in./min. | 80 sec |
| 1.5 | 40 |
| 3 | 20 |
| 6 | 10 |
| 12 | 5 |

Hence, we may use as a rule the following relation

$$\text{Time (in seconds) at 1 in. mark} = \frac{60}{\text{paper speed}} \qquad (3.13)$$

This relation obviously applies only to the particular strip-chart recorder discussed in Appendix A. It is very important to record the speed setting used in running a problem. If the Analog Computer Worksheet (Figure 3.1) is used, this entry should go under the column heading of Arm in the lower left-hand corner block. The entry under Pen is always 10, corresponding to the setting we always use for the recorder range switch (see Figure A.5). Generally, we label the value of time, in seconds, at every inch mark along the plot.

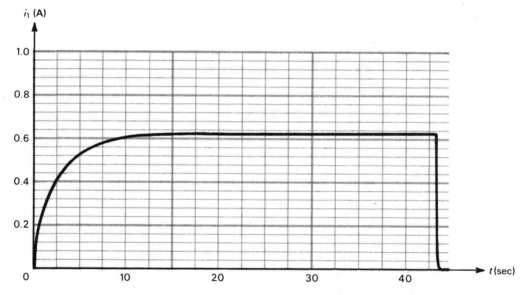

**Figure 3.8** *Plot for Example 3.2, current $i_1$ versus time t*

Other proper engineering graph techniques are always used in labeling computer plots. This includes a proper title block. The vertical (transverse) axes are labeled in terms of the variable plotted and the appropriate scale values are clearly shown. An example of a properly labeled computer plot is shown in Figure 3.8. This is a plot of the results of Example 3.2. We will have more to say about labeling of graphs after we discuss magnitude and time scaling.

The technique of indirect programming discussed in Section 3.1 often requires the availability of some arbitrary forcing function. In both the previous examples of this chapter, we required a step function input which we obtained with a pot whose input came from the computer reference supply. Often, more sophisticated forcing functions are required. Of special interest are exponential and sinusoidal forcing functions. We will develop programs to generate these functions, and others, in this section.

In the implicit programming of some arbitrary function, one first "discovers" the differential equation to which the desired function is a solution. This is done by successive differentiation of the function and substitution, until a differential equation is derived whose solution must be the function one started with. Then, the resulting differential equation is programmed using the indirect method discussed in Section 3.1. As before, a series of examples, of increasing complexity, illustrate this programming technique.

**example 3.3**

For this first example we program the step function. (We have already shown specific examples of its application.) Strictly speaking, the step function is a poor example of implicit programming, because of its trivial nature. The function is

$$x_f = Au_{-1}(t) \tag{3.14}$$

where $A < 1$; its plot is shown in Figure 3.9. The computer program is shown

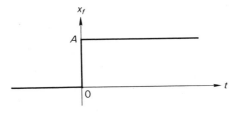

**Figure 3.9**

in Figure 3.10. The input is $+$ or $-$ depending on the desired sign on $x_f$. The input comes from the computer reference supply.

**Figure 3.10**

**example 3.4**

Consider the ramp function

$$x_f = At + x_f(0) \tag{3.15}$$

where $x_f(0) = B$. The constants $A$ and $B$ are both positive and less than unity; $A$ determines the slope of the ramp and $B$ determines the initial value. Using the implicit programming technique, we differentiate $x_f$ to "discover" the differential equation

$$\dot{x}_f = A \qquad (3.16)$$

This requires that we simply integrate a constant to obtain $x_f$. The IC is obtained in the usual way. The program is as shown in Figure 3.11.

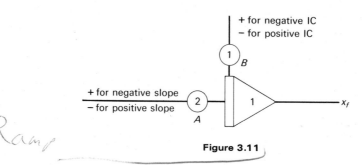

Ramp

**Figure 3.11**

We obviously can only allow the integrator to operate until its output reaches $+$ or $-$ unity. Hence, if $B = 0$ and $A = 0.010$, we can integrate for 100 sec. If $x_f(0) = -1$ (that is, pot 1 would not be used and the IC input would come from $+$ reference) and pot 2 (P2) is again 0.010, we can integrate for 200 sec. The ramp function program, used in this manner, is called a time base generator (TBG). The TBG is not needed with a strip recorder but it is sometimes necessary if an $X$-$Y$ plotter is used with the computer to obtain time recordings.

**example 3.5**

Consider the sinusoidal function

$$x_f = A \sin \omega t \qquad (3.17)$$

where $x_f(0) = 0$. Then,

$$\dot{x}_f = A\omega \cos \omega t \qquad (3.18)$$

with

$$\dot{x}_f(0) = A\omega$$

and

$$\ddot{x}_f = -A\omega^2 \sin \omega t = -\omega^2 x_f \qquad (3.19)$$

Thus, the differential equation we must program is

$$\ddot{x}_f + \omega^2 x_f = 0 \qquad (3.20)$$

Using indirect programming, we have

$$-\ddot{x}_f = \omega^2 x_f \qquad (3.21)$$

The computer flow diagram is shown in Figure 3.12. This program works for

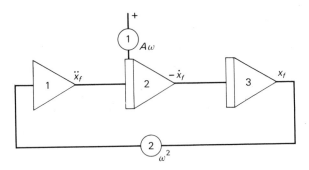

Figure 3.12

A and $\omega$ less than unity, but it is not too convenient to adjust, because of the product terms for the settings of the pots. The reader should verify that the program in Figure 3.13 is also correct, and that this program is also easier and more flexible to use. This last program can always be used to generate sine

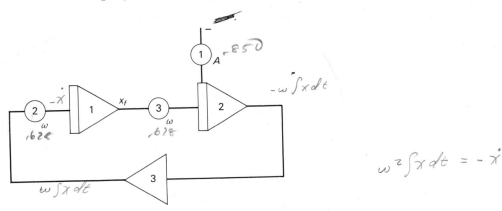

Figure 3.13

*or* cosine. We note that the output of A2 is + cosine and the output of A3 is − cosine. If the IC is moved to A1 we have + sine at A3, − sine at A2, and + cosine at A1.

### example 3.6

For this example, assume that we need the exponential function

$$x_f = Ae^{-\alpha t} \qquad (3.22)$$

Using implicit programming, we may derive the differential equation

$$\dot{x}_f + \alpha x_f = 0 \qquad (3.23)$$

where

$$x_f(0) = A$$

Normal indirect programming would result in a requirement for three amplifiers, but (3.23) can be solved using only one integrator as shown in Figure

3.14. In this program $A$ and $\alpha$ are again less than unity. If $A \ll 1$, one should use an IC of $-1$ and put P1 after A1. Also, $-x_f$ may be obtained by simply using a $+$IC.

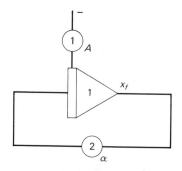

Figure 3.14

## example 3.7

As another example of the implicit programming of an exponential type function, consider the "gust" function (useful, for instance, in aerodynamic studies)

$$x_f = Ate^{-\alpha t} \qquad (3.24)$$

This function is sketched as in Figure 3.15. The quantity $A/\alpha e$ must be less

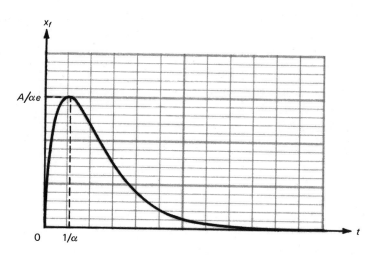

Figure 3.15

than unity in this unscaled example. The reader can, by differentiating (3.24) once and substituting, derive

$$\dot{x}_f + \alpha x_f = Ae^{-\alpha t} \qquad (3.25)$$

$$x_f(0) = 0$$

Finally, $x_f$ can be obtained from the program shown in Figure 3.16.

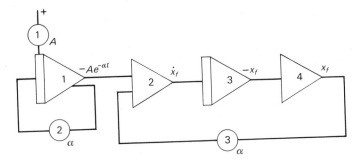

Figure 3.16

## example 3.8

This final example does not emphasize implicit programming techniques but it is included to complete the handling of types of functions frequently encountered in engineering systems analysis. We wish to examine the programming of the so-called unit impulse function $u_0(t)$. To do this, we use Laplace transform techniques, a mathematical representation with which we assume the reader to be familiar.

Before considering the programming of the impulse function, we briefly define this function and examine its properties. Much of the theory regarding this function is beyond the scope of this text; the reader is encouraged to consult any text on linear systems theory for a complete discussion. Also, the use of the notation of $u_0(t)$ is not unique, $\delta(t)$ for Dirac delta function is also commonly used. The sketch in Figure 3.17 is useful in considering the

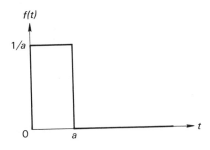

Figure 3.17

impulse function. We define this function to have unit area. Now, if we allow the width $a$ of this function to approach zero while maintaining constant area, the height $1/a$ approaches infinity. The resulting limiting pulse is called the unit impulse function. If we had started with a height $A/a$ and width $a$, an impulse of area $A$ would result. In the limit, this function would be called an impulse of "strength" $A$. The impulse function is a mathematical artifice that conveniently describes certain phenomena that occur in nature, for instance, the instantaneous transfer of electrical charge, beam bending, etc.

It can be shown by a limiting process involving the Laplace transform of step functions used to describe the impulse that the Laplace transform of $u_0(t)$ is unity. In general, the transform of any impulse function is equal to its strength. This point is emphasized because we take advantage of this fact in programming the impulse. To see this, consider the differential equation

$$\ddot{x} + B\dot{x} + Cx = Au_0(t) \tag{3.26}$$

Remembering the form of the operational transform for derivatives, and based on the above discussion, we may write the Laplace transform of (3.26) as

$$[s^2 X(s) - sx(0^+) - \dot{x}(0^+)] + B[sX(s) - x(0^+)] + CX(s) = A \tag{3.27}$$

The terms $x(0^+)$ and $\dot{x}(0^+)$ represent initial conditions. Assume that the initial conditions are

$$\dot{x}(0) = D$$
$$x(0) = 0 \tag{3.28}$$

We may then write (3.27) as

$$[s^2 X(s) - D] + B[sX(s)] + CX(s) = A \tag{3.29}$$

Since both $D$ and $A$ are constant, we can regroup (3.29) as

$$[s^2 X(s) - (D + A)] + BsX(s) + CX(s) = 0 \tag{3.30}$$

The quantity $D + A$ appears exactly as it would if it was the IC on $\dot{x}$ in the *homogeneous* equation

$$\ddot{x} + B\dot{x} + Cx = 0 \tag{3.31}$$

Hence, we conclude that one may program the impulse by simply programming the associated homogeneous equation and then placing an IC on the $(n - 1)$st integrator equal to the strength of the scaled impulse plus whatever normal IC may have been there already. We assumed that appropriate magnitude scaling of (3.26) had been achieved. The quantity $D + A$ must be a number less than unity.

The six examples just considered should allow the reader to progress to the implicit programming of any function the problem may require. It should be pointed out that the differential equation from which the desired function is obtained must, in general, be magnitude scaled. Functions such as sine, cosine, and the exponential are automatically magnitude scaled since their maximum value is unity, but other functions may have maximums appreciably greater than unity. We discuss magnitude scaling in the next chapter.

## PROBLEMS

**3.1.** The handling of initial conditions on integrators in the solution of differential equations is a very common source of error. Go through Example 3.1 very carefully and verify that the IC of

$$\dot{x}(0) = -0.3 \text{ m/sec}$$

has been correctly handled on integrator number 2. Start at amplifier number 4 and work backwards to show that the correct input to pot number 4 should be negative computer reference.

**3.2.** Assume, in Example 3.1, another initial condition of

$$x(0) = -0.2 \text{ m}$$

Show the modification that would have to be made to the flow diagram to account for this IC.

**3.3.** Use the final value theorem to confirm the results of Equation (3.6). Start with (3.2), write the transfer function (output over input, in the Laplace domain), solve for $X(s)$, and then apply the theorem.

**3.4.** A special notation is used throughout this text to define the unit impulse, step, and ramp functions. The subscript denotes the order of differentiation of the unit impulse. Thus, the step function $u_{-1}(t)$ is the "minus-first" derivative (that is, the first integral) of the unit impulse. Using Laplace transform operations, show that the following definitions are consistent with the above statements:

$u_0(t) \triangleq$ unit impulse function

$u_{-1}(t) \triangleq$ unit step function

$u_{-2}(t) \triangleq$ unit ramp function

**3.5.** The simple electrical network of Example 3.2 had two energy storage elements (the inductors $L_1$ and $L_2$). The program for this network required two integrators. As a general rule, the number of integrators should equal the number of energy storage elements. Write the Kirchhoff current law equation for the two-loop circuit in Figure 3.18 and confirm the fact that only one integrator is required to program the equation.

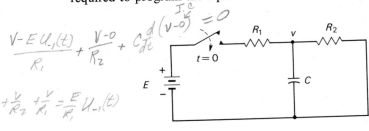

$$\frac{V - E u_{-1}(t)}{R_1} + \frac{V - 0}{R_2} + C\frac{d}{dt}(v - 0) = 0$$

$$+\frac{v}{R_2} + \frac{v}{R_1} = \frac{E}{R_1}u_{-1}(t)$$

$$\dot{v} + \left(\frac{R_1 + R_2}{CR_1 R_2}\right)v = \frac{1}{R_1 C}E u_{-1}(t)$$

1st order

**Figure 3.18**

**3.6.** Develop the flow diagram for the circuit of Problem 3.5. Assume that the initial voltage across the capacitor is zero. Since no values are given, simply show pot settings in terms of the given elements $E$, $C$, $R_1$, and $R_2$. Use the indirect → solve for neg. H.O. programming technique.

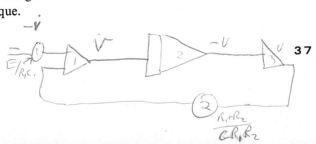

$$\dot{v} = \left(\frac{R_1 + R_2}{CR_1 R_2}\right)V\left(\frac{E}{R_1 C}\right)u_{-1}(t)$$

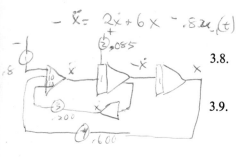

$$-\ddot{x} = 2\dot{x} + 6x - .8u_{-1}(t)$$

$\frac{+}{3}.085$

3.7. Arrange the following equation in the proper form for indirect programming. Assume that magnitude and time scaling (the subject of later chapters) are not required.

$$6.0\dot{x} + 3.0\ddot{x} + 18.0x = 2.4u_{-1}(t)$$
$$\dot{x}(0) = +0.085 \quad \text{make up second initial condition maybe } x = 0$$

3.8. Develop an analog flow diagram to solve the equation given in Problem 3.7. Are any gains 10 required to program the equation as stated?

3.9. Can you suggest a reason why amplifier number 4 was placed "ahead" of pot 1 in the program for Example 3.1? Would it make any difference if these two linear computing elements were interchanged?

3.10. What is the equation which is being solved by an analog computer wired as shown in Figure 3.19? What are the initial conditions?

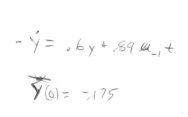

$$-\dot{y} = .6y + .89u_{-1}t$$

$$\dot{y}(0) = -.175$$

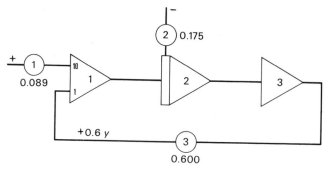

**Figure 3.19**

3.11. Write the expression for the output $z$ of the program shown in Figure 3.20, where $a$ and $b$ are constants, $x$ and $y$ are variables.

$$z = \frac{-x + 10by}{1 + 5a}$$

$$z = -(x - 10by + 15az)$$
$$= -x + 10by - 5az$$

$$z(1 + 5a) =$$

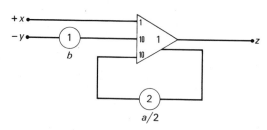

**Figure 3.20**

3.12. Sketch the four ramp functions possible using the program of Example 3.4. Show initial values and slopes.

3.13. Derive a second-order differential equation whose solution is the function given in Example 3.7. Develop the flow diagram, using indirect programming techniques. Do not worry about scaling at this point; show all pot settings in terms of $A$ and $\alpha$.

**38**   **introduction to programming**

3.14. Use implicit programming techniques to generate

$$x_f = At^2 e^{-\alpha t}$$

Show the flow diagram, assuming that no scaling is required.

3.15. Modify the sine–cosine generator developed in Example 3.5 to generate

$$x_f = A \sin(\omega t + \phi)$$

Show that, by proper choice of the initial conditions, both plus-and-minus sine or plus-and-minus cosine can be obtained from any one program.

# chapter four

We have mentioned several times that the mathematical model of any real physical system will almost certainly require magnitude scaling in order to be solvable on an analog computer. The examples we have so far considered were all carefully selected so that scaling was not necessary. This was done to emphasize basic concepts without unduly complicating the discussion. In fact, both magnitude *and* time scaling are generally required. We discuss the theory and application of magnitude scaling in this chapter and defer a discussion of time scaling to Chapter 6. The reader should realize, however, that scaling, both magnitude and time, is an integral part of the programming procedure and must always precede any machine operation.

Magnitude scaling is an algebraic, or arithmetic, operation performed on a system of differential equations to transform the dependent variables into analogous computer variables. Time scaling, on the other hand, is carried out on the computer, not on the equations, and involves a transformation from "real problem time" to a new "computer run time," the computer solution is speeded up, or slowed down.

There are several different techniques in use for both magnitude and time scaling. We will magnitude scale by the method of normalized variables (as mentioned in Chapter 1). Other techniques to be equivalent must obviously

# magnitude scaling

yield the same results; primary among them is the use of the so-called dimensional scale factors. Normalized variables are much easier to master than other methods of magnitude scaling and offer a quicker and more systematic approach to the actual machine operation.

The approach of indirect and implicit programming (Chapter 3), clearly requires magnitude scaling for almost any equation we attempt to program. This is true because the numerical coefficients of each of the derivative terms in our equation are formed using pots and/or amplifier input gains. Even if we use several gain 10 amplifiers (which, at least in the case of integrators, is generally not a good practice), we are limited to coefficients that are less than 10. Furthermore, even if the coefficients of these terms are less than unity, the maximum values of the variables themselves may be greater than unity. For example, consider the simple, first-order equation with zero initial condition

$$\dot{y} + 0.100y = 0.800u_{-1}(t) \tag{4.1}$$

We know that the maximum value of the dependent variable $y$ occurs where the slope $\dot{y}$ is zero; it is numerically equal to $0.800/0.100 = 8.0$. Hence, even though we could set the coefficients 0.100 and 0.800 on pots, the amplifier whose output was proportional to the variable $y$ would overload very quickly. This equation must be magnitude scaled before it can be programmed.

Another situation that obviously requires magnitude scaling is an equation where the coefficients cannot be obtained using pots and/or gains. This can be illustrated by a simple $RC$ circuit (Figure 4.1). If the switch is closed

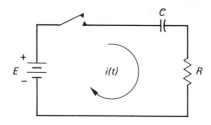

Figure 4.1    *RC circuit*

at time $t = 0$ in the presence of zero initial conditions and since $i = \dot{q}$, we have

$$\dot{q} + \frac{1}{RC}q = \frac{E}{R}u_{-1}(t) \tag{4.2}$$

If $R = 1\ \mathrm{k}\Omega$, $C = 0.1\ \mu\mathrm{F}$, and $E = 12\ \mathrm{V}$, we have

$$\dot{q} + 10{,}000q = 0.012u_{-1}(t) \tag{4.3}$$

Since this equation cannot be programmed in its present form, it too must be magnitude-scaled.

These two simple examples show the necessity for magnitude scaling. We now define terms and develop certain relationships that are useful in applying the method of normalized variables. We then go through several complete examples.

### 4.1 definitions and examples

We briefly mentioned the normalization of the integrator relation in Section 2.5; there we defined the bridging relation

$$\frac{y}{y_N} \triangleq x_y = \frac{e}{e_N} \tag{4.4}$$

We now need to define certain terms in order to understand normalized variables. If the dependent variable in our problem is $y$, we then *define* the *normalized variable* $x_y$ to be equal to the ratio of the original problem variable over its associated *normalizing constant* $y_N$. These ratios are defined for each term in the equation, independently of each other. Thus, we may have

$$x_y \triangleq \frac{y}{y_N}, \qquad \dot{x}_y \triangleq \frac{\dot{y}}{\dot{y}_N}, \qquad \ddot{x}_y \triangleq \frac{\ddot{y}}{\ddot{y}_N}, \qquad \ldots \tag{4.5}$$

The *normalizing constants* ($y_N$, $\dot{y}_N$, etc.) are chosen such that, in any given equation, they have the following properties:

(a) They are numbers, not variables.
(b) They carry the same dimensions (that is, volts, meters, BTU/sec, etc.) as the original problem variable with which they are associated.

(c) They are always positive.

(d) They are chosen to have a magnitude that is at least equal to, but preferably greater than, the expected maximum absolute value of the associated original problem variable.

Property (d) requires that we have some knowledge of, or can intelligently estimate the expected value of, the maximum absolute values of the variables in our problems. This is not always easy, although for simple cases we can develop methods for making good estimates; some of these techniques are discussed in Chapter 7. For this chapter, we simply assume that, based on an *a priori* knowledge of the system, we know approximately what the expected maximum values are, and we can thus choose normalizing constants.

From the definitions given by (4.5), we can list the following properties of *normalized variables*:

(a) They are variables, not numbers.

(b) They are always nondimensional.

(c) They always have the same algebraic sign as the original problem variable with which they are associated.

(d) They always have instantaneous values lying between plus and minus unity.

The reader should compare the properties of normalizing constants with the corresponding properties of normalized variables. The relationship that exists between these properties should be self-explanatory if one bears in mind the relations given by (4.5).

From our definition of the normalized variable $x_y$ (Equation (4.5)), we have

$$\frac{dx_y}{dt} = \frac{d}{dt}(x_y) \triangleq \frac{d}{dt}\left(\frac{y}{y_N}\right) \tag{4.6}$$

Since the normalizing constant $y_N$ is by definition a *constant*, we have

$$\frac{dx_y}{dt} = \frac{1}{y_N}\frac{d}{dt}(y) = \frac{1}{y_N}(\dot{y}) \tag{4.7}$$

Because $\dot{x}_y$ is also a *defined* quantity, we have

$$\dot{x}_y \triangleq \frac{\dot{y}}{\dot{y}_N} = \frac{1}{\dot{y}_N}(\dot{y}) \tag{4.8}$$

Comparing (4.7) and (4.8), we see that

$$\dot{x}_y \neq \frac{dx_y}{dt} \tag{4.9}$$

This does not violate anything we have previously learned, but is, of course, due to the fact that both $x_y$ and $\dot{x}_y$ are independently defined quantities.

After we developed the defining voltage relationships for the inverting, summing, and integrating amplifiers in Chapter 2, we normalized each expression by forming the ratio $e/e_N$ for each term. In this ratio the voltage $e$ may represent (be analogous to) any general problem variable $y$. Since $e_N = +10$ V (for 10-V machines) and since the design range of such a machine requires that $-10$ V $\leq e \leq +10$ V, we see that $-1 \leq e/e_N \leq +1$. In our problems, if we then form the ratio of $y/y_N$ such that $-1 \leq y/y_N \leq +1$, we will in fact have a normalized variable $x_y = y/y_N$ at the output of the amplifier whose voltage $e$ is analogous to the problem variable $y$. This entire discussion can be simply stated by Equation (2.27) or Equation (4.4).

We always label our flow diagrams in terms of normalized variables. Since amplifier outputs are *ratios* of voltages, we never refer to such outputs as numbers of *volts* but refer to them only as *numbers*.

For notational purposes, the subscript of the normalized variable denotes the original problem variable. For instance, for two dependent variables $y$ and $z$ in a problem, we would define

$$x_y \triangleq \frac{y}{y_N}, \qquad \dot{x}_y \triangleq \frac{\dot{y}}{\dot{y}_N}, \qquad \ldots \tag{4.10}$$

and

$$x_z \triangleq \frac{z}{z_N}, \qquad \dot{x}_z \triangleq \frac{\dot{z}}{\dot{z}_N}, \qquad \ldots \tag{4.11}$$

This allows us to always reserve the symbol $x$ for the normalized variable. We have followed this procedure throughout this text. Any equation written in terms of the variable $x$ is then a magnitude-scaled equation. Conversely, unscaled equations, such as (4.1) and (4.2), are never written in terms of $x$. After scaling, the dependent variable in those two equations would be $x_y$ and $x_q$, respectively.

The actual algebraic mechanics of scaling an equation are developed in the form of several examples which follow. Before proceeding to these examples, however, we need to examine the effect that magnitude scaling has on linear computing elements.

Simple inverting and coefficient amplifiers invert the normalized-variable input and, in the case of the latter, multiply it by a gain factor. The algebra associated with the summing amplifier is almost as simple and may be illustrated as follows. Suppose we seek to add two original problem variables $u$ and $v$, whose sum is defined to be the variable $w$. We have

$$u + v = -w \tag{4.12}$$

Each term must be normalized in accordance with our definitions. To do this and to maintain equality, we multiply and divide by the appropriate normalizing constants,

$$u_N \left(\frac{u}{u_N}\right) + v_N \left(\frac{v}{v_N}\right) = -w_N \left(\frac{w}{w_N}\right) \tag{4.13}$$

Since each parenthesized term is a normalized variable, we have

$$u_N x_u + v_N x_v = -w_N x_w \tag{4.14}$$

or, in terms of our desired sum,

$$-x_w = \left(\frac{u_N}{w_N}\right) x_u + \left(\frac{v_N}{w_N}\right) x_v \tag{4.15}$$

Assuming we have the normalized variables $x_u$ and $x_v$ available, we could obtain their sum with a program as shown in Figure 4.2. (We continue this illustration further in Example 4.1.) If, in relation (4.12), we sought the sum

$$K_1 u + K_2 v = -w \tag{4.16}$$

the pot settings in Figure 4.2 would be $K_1(u_N/w_N)$ for P1 and $K_2(v_N/w_N)$ for P2. Both, of course, must remain less than unity.

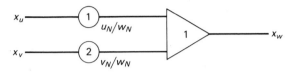

**Figure 4.2**   *Magnitude scaling of summer*

The effect of magnitude scaling on the integrator can be easily developed if we recall the relations developed in Section 2.5, and if we use inequality (4.9). If we want to integrate the normalized variable $\dot{x}$ so as to obtain the normalized variable $x$, we must obviously multiply by some factor to account for the inequality defined by (4.9). In other words, assuming a gain of unity on the integrator and calling the required multiplicative factor some $K$, we have

$$x_y = -K \int \dot{x}_y \, dt \tag{4.17}$$

Using the definitions, we may write

$$\frac{y}{y_N} = -K \int \frac{\dot{y}}{\dot{y}_N} \, dt \tag{4.18}$$

$$y = -K \frac{y_N}{\dot{y}_N} \int \dot{y} \, dt \tag{4.19}$$

$$= -K \frac{y_N}{\dot{y}_N} y \tag{4.20}$$

Obviously, for relation (4.20) to hold, we must have

$$K = \frac{\dot{y}_N}{y_N} \tag{4.21}$$

The negative sign is, of course, again due to the sign change in the amplifier. The results of (4.17) and (4.21) require the program of Figure 4.3 for an

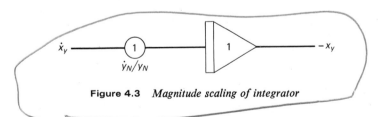

**Figure 4.3**   *Magnitude scaling of integrator*

integrator (assume zero IC for convenience). In a similar fashion, if we sought to obtain $\dot{x}_y$ from $-\ddot{x}_y$, we would require a pot set to the ratio $\ddot{y}_N/\dot{y}_N$. These pots are referred to as *integrator input pots.* They are required in *every* program involving magnitude-scaled equations.

This discussion has provided the necessary foundation for us to be able now to undertake several comprehensive examples that illustrate and develop the algebraic mechanics of magnitude scaling. For our first example, we return to the simple illustration of obtaining the sum of two variables $u$ and $v$.

**example 4.1**

Suppose we allow $u$ and $v$ in (4.12) to be constant *numbers*, not variables. Most quantities we deal with are, of course, variables, but we use numbers here since they show the details of scaling equally as well and are easier to deal with. Besides, we know the answer in advance!

Let

$$u = 395 \qquad\qquad (4.22)$$
$$v = 1850$$

We must now choose normalizing constants $u_N$ and $v_N$ consistent with properties (a) through (d) listed on pages 42–43. Hence, we could choose

$$u_N = 500 \qquad\qquad (4.23)$$
$$v_N = 2000$$

These are perfectly arbitrary choices, but they must be at least as large as $u$ and $v$, and preferably a "good number." We will have more to say about the choice of normalizing constants in Section 4.3. Following (4.13) and (4.14), we may write

$$500x_u + 2000x_v = -w_N x_w \qquad\qquad (4.24)$$

Now, we must estimate the maximum value of $w$ (the sum) so that we can choose $w_N$. This is obviously a trivial matter here because we know the value of $w$ exactly. However, assuming we did not know its value (which would be the usual case if $u$ and $v$ were variables), we would probably make a conservative estimate, based on $u_{\max}$ and $v_{\max}$, of, say, 5000. Choosing such a value for $w_N$ allows us to write (4.15) as

$$-x_w = \left(\frac{500}{5000}\right) x_u + \left(\frac{2000}{5000}\right) x_v \qquad\qquad (4.25)$$

or

$$-x_w = 0.100x_u + 0.400x_v \qquad\qquad (4.26)$$

Now, as shown in Figure 4.2, we could obtain the normalized sum $x_w$ if we had available $x_u$ and $x_v$. These terms would usually be generated elsewhere in our program but, in this simple case, they too are just constants. Specifically,

$$x_u \triangleq \frac{u}{u_N} = \frac{395}{500} = 0.790 \qquad\qquad (4.27)$$

and

$$x_v \triangleq \frac{v}{v_N} = \frac{1850}{2000} = 0.925 \qquad\qquad (4.28)$$

In terms of Figure 4.2, our program would be as shown in **Figure 4.4**. From

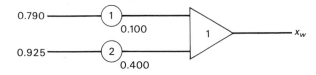

**Figure 4.4**

this program we obtain the program shown in **Figure 4.5**. If we were to patch

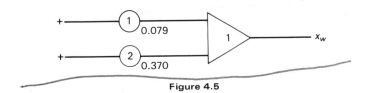

**Figure 4.5**

this program and run it (the reader is encouraged to do so), we would read A1 as

$$x_w = -0.449 \tag{4.29}$$

Now, to find the sum $w$, we recall the definition of $x_w$ and, considering the sign change in the amplifier, we have

$$w = x_w w_N \tag{4.30}$$

or

$$w = (0.449)(5000) = 2245 \tag{4.31}$$

which we, of course, knew to be the correct answer all along. However, the purpose of this simple exercise in scaling was not to prove simple arithmetic, but rather to illustrate magnitude-scaling techniques using the concept of normalized variables. The next example is more realistic in terms of a real system equation.

*example 4.2*

Let us assume that we have analyzed a rotational mechanical system and have developed the following differential equation and IC,

$$12\ddot{\theta} + 5.04\dot{\theta} + 5.88\theta = 432u_{-1}(t) \tag{4.32}$$
$$\dot{\theta}(0) = -75 \text{ rad/sec}, \qquad \theta(0) = 0$$

We seek a solution to this equation and we also want a record of $\ddot{\theta}$, $\dot{\theta}$, and $\theta$ versus $t$. Even after dividing through by the coefficient on $\ddot{\theta}$ and obtaining

$$\ddot{\theta} + 0.42\dot{\theta} + 0.49\theta = 36u_{-1}(t) \tag{4.33}$$

we note that this equation obviously requires magnitude scaling because of the IC and the forcing function. Based on *a priori* knowledge of the physical system, we assume that we know the following maximum magnitudes for the variables:

$$|\theta|_{max} = 116 \text{ rad}, \qquad |\dot\theta|_{max} = 75 \text{ rad/sec}, \qquad |\ddot\theta|_{max} = 72 \text{ rad/sec}^2 \tag{4.34}$$

We then could choose the following normalizing constants:

$$\theta_N = 125 \text{ rad}, \qquad \dot\theta_N = 100 \text{ rad/sec}, \qquad \ddot\theta_N = 75 \text{ rad/sec}^2 \tag{4.35}$$

Using these values, we magnitude scale Equation (4.33) and obtain first

$$\ddot\theta_N \left(\frac{\ddot\theta}{\ddot\theta_N}\right) + 0.420\dot\theta_N \left(\frac{\dot\theta}{\dot\theta_N}\right) + 0.490\theta_N \left(\frac{\theta}{\theta_N}\right) = 36u_{-1}(t) \tag{4.36}$$

and, secondly,

$$\ddot\theta_N \ddot x_\theta + 0.420\dot\theta_N \dot x_\theta + 0.490\theta_N x_\theta = 36u_{-1}(t) \tag{4.37}$$

and, thirdly,

$$\ddot x_\theta + \frac{(0.420)(100)}{75}\dot x_\theta + \frac{(0.490)(125)}{75}x_\theta = \frac{36}{75}u_{-1}(t) \tag{4.38}$$

The final magnitude-scaled equation and IC are therefore

$$\ddot x_\theta + 0.560\dot x_\theta + 0.817 x_\theta = 0.480u_{-1}(t) \tag{4.39}$$

$$\dot x_\theta(0) = \frac{\dot\theta(0)}{\dot\theta_N} = -\frac{75}{100} = -0.750 \tag{4.40}$$

We know that we can program this equation because every pot setting can be attained and, by the very definition of the term, no normalized variable exceeds plus or minus unity. The reader should verify that the flow diagram of Figure

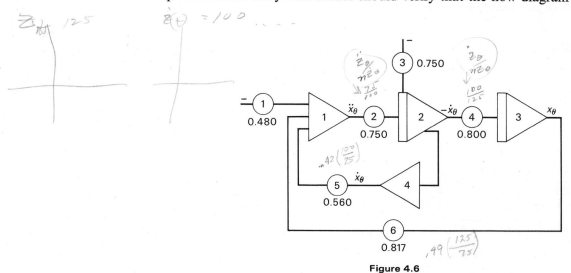

**Figure 4.6**

4.6 represents the correct program for the magnitude-scaled equation (4.39) and IC (4.40).

The integrator input pots, P2 and P4, are found by the method discussed in the text in the development of Figure 4.3. They are calculated to be

$$P2 = \frac{\ddot{\theta}_N}{\dot{\theta}_N} = \frac{75}{100} = 0.750$$

$$P4 = \frac{\dot{\theta}_N}{\theta_N} = \frac{100}{125} = 0.800$$

(4.41)

Integrator input pots should *always* be inserted in a program. If the ratios to which they are to be set are exactly 1.00, then one should set the pots to 0.100 and connect them to gain 10 on the following integrators. The inclusion of integrator input pots allows one to perform magnitude rescaling while on the computer. This procedure will be discussed in Section 4.2.

The system described by (4.33) in Example 4.2 has $\zeta = 0.3$ and $\omega_n = 0.7$ rad/sec. The reader can verify on the computer that the following maximums are reached

$$|x_\theta|_{max} \cong 0.93 \Rightarrow |\theta|_{max} = |x_\theta|_{max}\theta_N = (0.93)(125) = 116 \text{ rad}$$
$$|\dot{x}_\theta|_{max} \cong 0.75 \Rightarrow |\dot{\theta}|_{max} = |\dot{x}_\theta|_{max}\dot{\theta}_N = (0.75)(100) = 75 \text{ rad/sec}$$
$$|\ddot{x}_\theta|_{max} \cong 0.96 \Rightarrow |\ddot{\theta}|_{max} = |\ddot{x}_\theta|_{max}\ddot{\theta}_N = (0.96)(75) = 72 \text{ rad/sec}^2$$

(4.42)

Example 4.2 was well-scaled because our choice of the normalizing constants given in (4.35) was based on an exact knowledge of the maximums obtainable in our equation. Without such information, we would make more conservative (larger) estimates for the normalizing constants, and as a result the variations of the computer variables would not be as large as they are in this example. In general, if the maximum magnitude of a normalized variable is about 0.5 or larger (occupies 50% of the available plotting area), we may conclude that we have a reasonably well-scaled problem. This introduces the possible necessity for rescaling a problem if the original estimates of maximums were significantly in error; this is discussed in the next section.

**4.2 magnitude rescaling**

We have discussed the fact that normalizing constants in a problem are chosen to be equal to, or slightly greater than, the expected maximum values of the original problem variables. If the maximums are known (as they have been in the examples considered so far) or if they can be estimated quite closely, then the normalized variables defined by (4.5) always occupy most of the range between plus and minus unity. In other words, we have well-scaled problems if the amplifier outputs use a significant portion of the design range of the computer.

However, if the maximums are not well-defined or cannot be estimated very accurately, we may make bad choices for the normalizing constants and one or more amplifiers may overload or, conversely, may have outputs so small that poor computing accuracy results. The former is caused by choosing normalizing constants too small; whereas the latter results from choosing the constants too large. Both these situations can occur, although, in practice, it is certainly better to make conservative (large) estimates for maximums in order to avoid overloads. If either situation occurs, we might need to adjust our magnitude scaling while on the computer in order to bring the outputs of one or more amplifiers to within acceptable levels. This can be done very easily for any given amplifier in the program without affecting the other computing elements. The following example illustrates a specific application of the procedure used.

### example 4.3

Suppose in programming Example 4.2 we had made a bad estimate for $\theta_{max}$ and, as a result, we had chosen $\theta_N$ to be 375 rad instead of 125 rad. (375 is not a "good" number, as we will see in Section 4.3, but assume we had chosen it here.) From (4.38) and (4.41) we see that we would have required the following settings

$$P6 = \frac{(0.490)(375)}{75}$$

$$= 2.45 = (10)(0.245)$$

$$P4 = \frac{100}{375} = 0.267 \qquad (4.43)$$

To achieve 2.45 we would set P6 to 0.245 and use a gain 10 input on A1. With this program, the reader can confirm that we would read a maximum output from A3 of about 0.31. The other amplifier outputs are as listed in (4.42). We note this small value for the output of A3 and decide to improve it.

To do this, we would have to increase the output of just A3 and not change anything else. Since A3 reads 0.31, we could increase its output by a factor of 3 without reaching an overload condition. To increase the output of A3 we would have to increase its input gain by a factor of 3. Since the net input gain includes the gain 1 input and the setting of P4, and since we have no "gain 3" inputs, we would increase P4 to (3) (0.267), or 0.800. Since P4 is set to $\dot\theta_N/\theta_N$, this means we have simply decreased $\theta_N$ by a factor of 3 (from 375 to 125). In order not to affect the rest of the program, we would have to keep the output of P6 the same as before. Since we had increased the A3 output by 3, we would have to reduce the setting of P6 by a factor of 3. This would reduce it to 0.817. With these new settings we would, of course, have the program we used in Example 4.2. The output of A3 is a normalized 0.93.

We can generalize the above technique into a procedure termed the *Double-and-Halve Rule*, and we can apply this rule to any amplifier in a magnitude-scaled program to either increase (or decrease) its output. We need not use a factor of 2 (we used 3 in Example 4.3), but we quote the rule in terms of 2. The rule may be stated as follows:

To double (halve) the normalizing constant associated with the normalized variable appearing at an amplifier output, and hence to halve (double) the output, we halve (double) the input gains and double (halve) the output gains.

The input gains referred to are those immediately preceding the amplifier in question (and this *includes* any IC), and the output gains are those immediately following the amplifier. In some cases the application of this rule may require the insertion of a pot where none had been programmed. This is another reason why we stated earlier that integrator input pots should always be included in our programs.

An important thing to remember in applying the double-and-halve rule, and a very common source of error, is to record all of the changes made in a program. Without such a record one has no knowledge of the final choice of normalizing constants and, as a result, the answers cannot be correctly interpreted. Records of doubling and halving should be entered directly on the flow diagram.

## 4.3 choice of normalizing constants

Normalizing constants are chosen based on estimates of the maximum values of our problem variables, and they have the properties listed in Section 4.1. Since they are used in the interpretation of the computer results, and since their choice affects the arithmetic of the scaling procedure, it is advantageous to use so-called "good" numbers for normalizing constants. We will see in the next section, when we discuss the labeling of computer plots, that numbers that are easily divisible by 5 are very "good." Hence, we should consider numbers such as

5, 10, 25, 50, 75, 100, . . .

or power-of-10 multiples of these. Other numbers may also be acceptable in any given situation, but to a large extent the choice depends upon the recording equipment and/or graph paper being used. We will see how this fact applies in the next section.

## 4.4 interpretation of plots

The results of an analog-computer solution of a problem almost always takes the form of a graphical record. We have already discussed some aspects of the labeling of strip-recorder plots in Section 3.2. We gave a rule (relation 3.13) there for the labeling of the horizontal (time) axis for a particular recorder. In this section we discuss the labeling and scales used on the vertical (transverse) axis. We seek a rule, analogous to (3.13) for the time axis, which we can use to interpret properly and easily the labeling of the plots of magnitude-scaled variables.

The first point we should emphasize is that computer plots are never labeled in terms of the normalized variable. For instance, in Example 4.2, we might want to record the variable $\theta$ versus $t$. We addressed A3 in the flow diagram (Figure 4.6) in terms of $x_\theta$, but we would label our plot in terms of $\theta$, *not* $x_\theta$. This kind of error is common, but it is avoided if one always remembers the original variables in the unscaled equation.

The scale values that we put along the vertical axis are directly related to our choice of normalizing constants. The recorder range controls are adjusted such that the recorder pen experiences full scale, positive deflection when the computing amplifier to which it is connected reaches a full $+10$ V (or $-10$ V) or normalized $+1$ (or $-1$), output. We will discuss the setting of the recorder range switch in Appendix A. We know from the definitions of normalized variables that an amplifier reaches full normalized plus or minus unity when the problem variable (say $\theta$) is exactly equal to the normalizing constant $\theta_N$. Thus, if we reach full scale recorder deflection with the recorder range switch set on 10, we know that the variable is exactly equal to the associated normalizing constant. This means we can simply mark the maximum points on our vertical scale to be plus the normalizing constant and minus the normalizing constant at the top and bottom, respectively. Since the normalizing constants always have the same dimensions (units) as the variable being plotted, there is little chance of incorrectly marking the scale if we follow the above rule.

To summarize the labeling of plots of magnitude-scaled variables, consider Figure 4.7. Assume that we have plotted some general variable $y$ having the unit of meters. The plot was made on the particular recorder discussed in

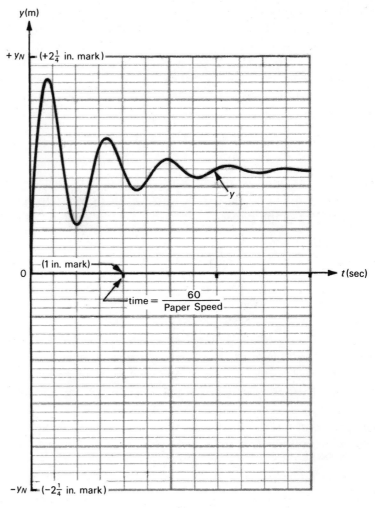

**Figure 4.7**  *Labeling of computer plot*

Appendix A. The recording paper on this machine is $4\frac{1}{2}$ in. wide (writing area) and, depending upon the type of paper used, there are four or five major divisions on each side of zero (center). The vertical scale would be labeled as shown. The actual *value* of $y_N$ (not the symbol) would be entered. Also, the values at the major subdivisions on the vertical axis would be shown. Note the labeling of the time axis as given by (3.13) in Section 3.2.

It should be clear from the above discussion that our plots are much easier to interpret if we choose "good" numbers for our normalizing constants. Thus, if we use recorder paper with five major divisions on either side of zero, the numbers given in Section 4.3 would be very good. This is also something to keep in mind when magnitude rescaling using the double-and-halve rule has to be done.

In fact, the choice of 375 rad for $\theta_N$ in Example 4.3 was not, as was mentioned at the time, a very good choice. Using five-division paper, we would have 75 radians-per-major division but, using four-division paper, we would have 93.75 radians-per-division. The number 75 may be acceptable, but 93.75 certainly is not.

The comprehensive illustration of proper graph labeling given in Figure 4.7 is applicable to any plot made using the particular recorder discussed in Appendix A. The student can easily develop rules analogous to those illustrated in Figure 4.7 if he has available a different type of recorder. We make a simple addition to the labeling given in the figure when we discuss time scaling in Chapter 6; only the labeling of the time axis will be affected.

## PROBLEMS

4.1. Stability is an important concept in the programming of differential equations. Use the Routh-Hurwitz stability criterion to determine whether or not the systems described by the following characteristic equations are stable, unstable. or conditionally stable (poles on the imaginary axis).

    (a)   $s^5 + 4s^4 + 4s^3 + 4s^2 + 4s + 8 = 0$
    (b)   $s^4 + 10s + 10s^2 + 5s^3 + 4 = 0$
    (c)   $s^5 + s^4 + 4s^3 + 3s^2 + 4s + 2 = 0$

4.2. Given the characteristic system equation

$$s^3 + bs^2 + cs + d = 0$$

Determine the relation that must exist between the positive constants $b$, $c$, and $d$ in order for the system to be stable. Discuss the location of the poles if $bc = d$.

4.3. The programming of the function $Ate^{-at}$ used in Example 3.7 involves a knowledge of the maximum value of $x_f$ and $\dot{x}_f$, since both appear at amplifier outputs. Confirm the maximum value shown for $x_f$ and find the maximum value of $\dot{x}_f$, and the point at which it occurs.

4.4. Assume that an $X$-$Y$ recorder having a $Y$ axis sensitivity of 2 V/in. is used with a 10-V computer to plot the results of Problem 4.7. What values should be placed at the 5-in. mark for the ordinates of the plots of $\ddot{z}$, $\dot{z}$, and $z$? If the strip recorder discussed in Section A.5 is used with the same computer, how should the ordinates of these same plots be labeled?

4.5. Find the maximum value of the variables $q$ and $\dot{q}$ in Equation (4.3). Suggest values for $q_N$ and $\dot{q}_N$.

4.6. Given the following differential equation with initial conditions

$$\ddot{y} + 6\dot{y} + 9y = 36u_{-1}(t)$$
$$\dot{y}(0) = 0$$
$$y(0) = 0$$

Assuming normalizing constants have been chosen as follows, magnitude scale this equation.

$$y_N = 5 \text{ V}, \qquad \dot{y}_N = 5 \text{ V/sec}, \qquad \ddot{y}_N = 50 \text{ V/sec}^2$$

What would have to be done if non-zero initial conditions were present?

4.7. Given the following differential equation, with zero initial conditions and normalizing constants

$$3\ddot{z} + 2.4\dot{z} + 48z = 24u_{-1}(t)$$
$$z_N = 1 \text{ m}, \qquad \dot{z}_N = 2.5 \text{ m/sec}, \qquad \ddot{z}_N = 10 \text{ m/sec}^2$$

Magnitude scale this equation.

4.8. A third-order mechanical rotational system is described by the differential equation

$$250\dddot{\theta} + 1156.25\ddot{\theta} + 1100.0\dot{\theta} + 1562.5\theta = 92500u_{-1}(t)$$

with

$$\ddot{\theta}(0) = -40.0 \text{ rad/sec}^2$$
$$\dot{\theta}(0) = 82.5 \text{ rad/sec}$$
$$\theta(0) = 0$$

Based on experimental observations, the following normalizing constants have been selected:

$$\dddot{\theta}_N = 500 \text{ rad/sec}^3 \qquad \dot{\theta}_N = 100 \text{ rad/sec}$$
$$\ddot{\theta}_N = 100 \text{ rad/sec}^2 \qquad \theta_N = 100 \text{ rad}$$

Find the magnitude-scaled equation and initial conditions.

4.9. Develop the analog computer flow diagram for the system described in Problem 4.8. Do not overlook the requirement for integrator input pots. (Review the comment about including these pots even though the ratio to which they are to be set is equal to unity.)

4.10. Consider the $RC$ circuit shown in Figure 4.8 with parameters as given.
   (a) Write the Kirchhoff current law equation in terms of the voltage $v(t)$ at the node, as indicated.
   (b) Assume that normalizing constants are chosen to be

$$\dot{v}_N = 75 \text{ V/sec}, \quad v_N = 100 \text{ V}$$

Magnitude scale the equation of part (a). The initial voltage across the capacitor is zero.

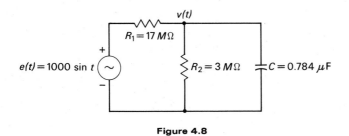

Figure 4.8

**4.11.** Develop the complete analog computer flow diagram to solve the circuit of Problem 4.10 for the voltage $v(t)$.

**4.12.** Given the magnitude-scaled simultaneous differential equations

$$\ddot{x}_1 + 0.410\dot{x}_1 + 2.10x_1 + 0.500\dot{x}_2 = 0$$
$$\dot{x}_2 + 0.530x_2 + 0.745\ddot{x}_1 = 0$$

with

$$\dot{x}_1(0) = -0.640$$
$$x_2(0) = +0.820$$

Develop the complete analog computer flow diagram to solve these equations. Assume that the ratios of all normalizing constants are unity.

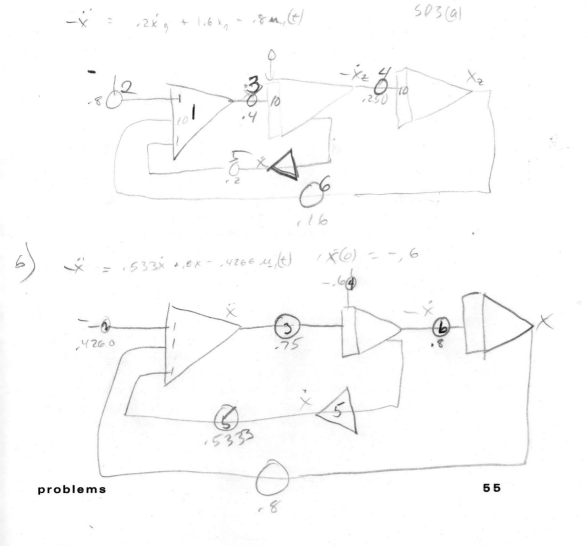

# chapter five

**5.0 introduction**
The magnitude-scaling and programming procedures discussed in the previous chapters, if correctly carried out, result in programs for the analog computer that solve our given problems. The programmer need only wire the computer patch panel or patch board and he will be ready to run the program to obtain the problem solution. However, many errors can enter into the scaling and/or programming work, especially if the analyst is faced with a comprehensive problem. Even if the scaling work is free of errors, wiring errors can be introduced when the problem is patched on the computer, or pots can easily be set to incorrect values. Conversely, all the programming and wiring can be correct but minor malfunctions of the equipment can destroy the accuracy of a solution. For these reasons, it is desirable to have simple, well-defined check procedures designed to uncover certain common scaling, wiring, or equipment problems.

In this chapter we discuss two common check procedures termed the *static check* and *program check*. We examine the purpose behind each of these checks and through comprehensive examples show how these check procedures are calculated for a representative problem. The reader should recognize that the basic purpose behind each check is to aid the programmer in assessing whether or not his problem has been correctly prepared to obtain an analog computer solution.

# check procedures

The static check is a two-step arithmetic procedure that is designed to uncover errors made in wiring a computer program. When properly calculated and confirmed on the computer, this check assures the programmer that his flow diagram has been correctly connected on the computer. Since wiring and/or pot setting errors are a common source of difficulty to both the novice and the experienced programmer, this check can be a very useful tool. One should not proceed to actual computer operation until a satisfactory static check has been obtained.

The *calculation* of the static check is the first step in its application. This is done as soon as a flow diagram has been prepared. One side of the particular type of Analog Computer Worksheet shown in Figure 3.1 can be used for the flow diagram. Then the static check can be calculated using the space provided. We will see the use of this worksheet in Example 5.1.

The static check is calculated assuming the computer is in the RESET, or IC, mode. The numerical output of every amplifier and pot in the program is then calculated and entered in the appropriate space on the worksheet (Figure 3.1). Pots simply multiply their input by some positive constant less than unity in the IC mode and summers algebraically sum (and invert) their inputs in this mode. Integrators, however, have as their outputs only the negative of their

IC inputs; all normal inputs are disconnected. For further comments on this the reader is encouraged to study Section A.2. Thus, to calculate integrator outputs for the static check, we must be concerned only with the IC involved. If the problem being solved does not require initial conditions on every integrator (that is, some IC's are zero), we *add* what we call "FALSE" IC's. These FALSE IC's are actually wired into our program and are used to check those parts of the flow diagram wiring that would not otherwise be checked. Obviously, the FALSE IC's must be removed before actual problem solving begins. The application of FALSE IC's and the notation we use to ensure their removal are covered in detail in Example 5.1.

The second step in the static check procedure is the *performance* of the check on the computer. Having calculated the numerical output of every amplifier and pot in our program, we then go on the computer and, by checking certain key amplifiers and pots, we perform the check. A satisfactory static check is obtained when we achieve close agreement between our calculated and observed readings.

This brief introduction to the static check process is made clearer by a comprehensive example. We go through the complete static check procedure in Example 5.1, and then in Example 5.2 we return to the same system and illustrate the calculation of the program check.

### example 5.1

This example illustrates the calculation of a static check for a system described by

$$2\ddot{z} + 10\ddot{z} + 6\dot{z} + 15z = 70u_{-1}(t) \tag{5.1}$$

with

$$\begin{aligned} \ddot{z}(0) &= -5.0 \text{ m/sec}^2 \\ \dot{z}(0) &= +7.5 \text{ m/sec} \\ z(0) &= 0 \end{aligned} \tag{5.2}$$

Assume that enough is known regarding the physical system so that we can estimate the following maxima

$$\begin{aligned} |\dddot{z}|_{\max} &= 37.4 \text{ m/sec}^3 & |\dot{z}|_{\max} &= 7.5 \text{ m/sec} \\ |\ddot{z}|_{\max} &= 7.0 \text{ m/sec}^2 & |z|_{\max} &= 8.8 \text{ m} \end{aligned} \tag{5.3}$$

Based on these maxima, we would probably choose

$$\begin{aligned} \dddot{z}_N &= 50 \text{ m/sec}^3 & \dot{z}_N &= 10 \text{ m/sec} \\ \ddot{z}_N &= 10 \text{ m/sec}^2 & z_N &= 10 \text{ m} \end{aligned} \tag{5.4}$$

The magnitude-scaled equation and initial conditions for this system are shown on the bottom part of the Analog Computer Worksheet (Figure 5.2). The flow diagram, from which the static check is calculated, is shown in Figure 5.1. Note the gains of 10 on A1, A2, A3, and A4. The reader can confirm that the integrator input pots P4 and P6 require a setting of 1.00; hence, we use 0.100

and a gain 10. P2 is calculated as 5.00, so we use 0.500 and gain 10. The coefficient on the $x_z$ term (1.50) requires that we also set P9 to 0.150 and use a gain

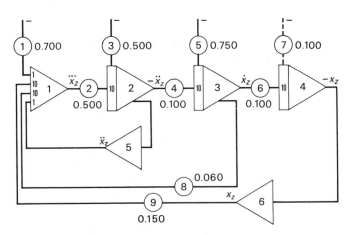

**Figure 5.1**

10 on A1. The other gain 10 on A1 is for convenience only, it eliminates borrowing other inputs. Note also, that, because $x_z(0)$ was zero, we use a FALSE IC (P7) on A4. The dotted line from computer reference, through P7, into the IC on A4, is used to denote the fact that the IC on A4 is a FALSE IC. The setting of P7 is arbitrary but is chosen as a round number (for easier arithmetical calculation) with a polarity so as not to cause A1 to overload. The algebraic sum of the step input (P1) plus the three feedback loops appears at the input to A1; hence the arbitrary choice of sign and magnitude of P7 could, if due care is not taken, result in a calculated output for A1 greater than unity. This is of course unacceptable for a static check calculation because it indicates an overload at time $t = 0$.

We can now calculate the static check using the Analog Computer Worksheet. Many blanks on this form are self-explanatory so no mention is made of them. We begin by entering the amplifier and pot numbers used in our program in the appropriate columns, Figure 5.2. The suggestion in the last paragraph of Section A.3 has been followed with regard to the listing of pot numbers. The polarity sign of P1, P3, P5, and P7 means that the inputs to these pots are obtained from computer reference and this is noted in the column headed "Pot setting." The amplifier output variables are entered as shown under "Output vari." Note carefully that pot number 7 is circled; this denotes the fact that P7 serves as a FALSE IC and *must be removed* prior to the running of the program to obtain the solution. We remove the FALSE IC by removing the input wire.

We can now begin placing entries for the numerical output of each pot in the column headed "Calc. value." The pot output is of course the numerical input value (with associated polarity) multiplied by the pot setting. For this computation we obviously ignore the polarity signs we put on the settings of P7, P3, P1, and P5. At this point we can enter every pot output except P2. P2 depends upon the calculated output of A1, and we do not obtain this value

| | | | STATIC CHECK | | | | | |
|---|---|---|---|---|---|---|---|---|
| **ANALOG COMPUTER WORKSHEET** Lab _____ | | | | | Name | | | |
| | | | | | Date | | Sect. | |
| | | | | | Course | | Prob. *Ex. 5.1* | |

| **Calculations** | Amp. no. | Output vari. | Calc. value | Meas. value | Pot no. | Pot setting | Calc. value | Meas. value |
|---|---|---|---|---|---|---|---|---|
| | 1 | $\dddot{x}_3$ | ⊕0.900 | | 8 | 0.060 | +0.045 | |
| $P1: -0.700$ | 2 | $-\ddot{x}_3$ | +0.500 | | 4 | 0.100 | +0.050 | |
| $10\,P9: -0.150$ | 3 | $\dot{x}_3$ | +0.750 | | 6 | 0.100 | +0.075 | |
| $10\,P8: +0.450$ | 4 | $-x_3$ | +0.100 | | ⑦ | -0.100 | -0.100 | |
| $A5: -0.500$ | 5 | $\ddot{x}_3$ | -0.500 | | 9 | 0.150 | -0.015 | |
| $\overline{\quad -0.900}$ | 6 | $x_3$ | -0.100 | | 2 | 0.500 | +0.450 | |
| Sign change | | | | | 3 | -0.500 | -0.500 | |
| $A1: +0.900$ | | | | | 1 | -0.700 | -0.700 | |
| | | | | | 5 | -0.750 | -0.750 | |

**Magnitude-Scaled Equations and Initial Conditions**

$$\dddot{x}_3 + \ddot{x}_3 + 0.600\,\dot{x}_3 + 1.50\,x_3 = 0.700\,u_{-1}(t)$$
$$\ddot{x}_3(0) = -0.500$$
$$\dot{x}_3(0) = +0.750$$
$$x_3(0) = 0$$

**Notes**

Static check for example 5.1

| Run | Plot | F1 | F2 | F3 | Sel. | Arm | Pen | n |
|---|---|---|---|---|---|---|---|---|
| 1 | $\dddot{x}_3$ vs. $t$ | — | — | — | A1 | 12 | 10 | — |
| 2 | $\ddot{x}_3$ vs. $t$ | — | — | — | A5 | 12 | 10 | — |
| 3 | $\dot{x}_3$ vs. $t$ | — | — | — | A3 | 12 | 10 | — |
| 4 | $x_3$ vs. $t$ | — | — | — | A6 | 12 | 10 | — |

**Normalizing Constants**

$$\dddot{x}_N = 50 \ m/sec^3$$
$$\ddot{x}_N = 10 \ m/sec^2$$
$$\dot{x}_N = 10 \ m/sec$$
$$x_N = 10 \ m$$

Figure 5.2

until we perform the same arithmetic (under the "Calculations" column) as is actually done by the summer. This arithmetic obviously depends on the output of P1, P8, P9, and A5.

The entries for the amplifier "Calc. value" column on the worksheet are calculated remembering that the only output of an integrator in the IC mode is the negative of its IC input; normal inputs are disconnected. The output of an inverter, such as A5, is the negative of its normal input. Thus, we should start with integrator outputs and then follow on around the loops. The reader is encouraged to go through the arithmetic, thereby obtaining every pot and amplifier output, except P2 and A1.

Having obtained the P1, P9, P8, and A5 outputs, we can perform the calculations necessary to obtain the A1 output. The "bookkeeping" is shown under the "Calculations" column and should be self-explanatory. One must keep in mind that we have two gain 10 inputs and, also, that the output is the negative (inverted) sum of the inputs. The calculated output of A1 is found to be +0.900. This value is entered and *circled* on the static check form. The circle means that we need check only this one reading when we perform the static check on the computer. If the actual value we observe for A1 is near our calculated value we can be certain that we have patched the great majority of our program correctly. The agreement between calculated and observed values for the outputs of "primary summers" (a name we can give to amplifiers such as A1 that sum the outputs of several feedback paths) should be very good. Depending upon the number of gain 10 amplifiers involved, we should, by using the null comparison method discussed in Appendix A, check our calculated output to within several digits in the third decimal place.

As mentioned earlier, if A1 checks when we perform the static check, then we know all the wiring associated with the step input and the three feedback loops is correct. We need to check physically the connections between the integrators, and the associated pot settings, because the static check procedure does not otherwise check this part of our patching. On some computers with installed digital voltmeters we can also read pot outputs. With such a machine, we would also circle the P2, P4, and P6 outputs, and we would check these values along with A1 when we performed the static check.

To summarize this procedure, we note that the static check is based on and is designed to check the correct patching of a flow diagram. It does *not* check our scaling calculations. We *calculate* a static check assuming the computer is in the RESET (IC) mode, and we *perform* the check on the computer in that mode. When we perform the static check, we enter on the form the observed outputs of those amplifiers whose calculated outputs we have circled. Agreement confirms the accuracy of our patching. Finally, we must remember to remove any FALSE IC's we may have used.

## 5.2 program check

The program check is the second of the two check procedures described in general terms in Section 5.0. It is designed to check the accuracy of all our scaling calculations, the flow diagram, and the static check calculations. We again have available a special form entitled the Program Check Worksheet that we use to calculate this check; we illustrate its use in Example 5.2.

The program check uses specific calculations from the static check and, by essentially working the magnitude-scaling calculations "backwards" (which we call unscaling, or descaling), it confirms our scaling work. Thus, just as with the static check, it is a powerful tool to aid the programmer in preparing a problem for a computer solution. Example 5.2 below illustrates the calculation of a program check.

### example 5.2

This example is a continuation of Example 5.1. We calculate a program check for the system described by (5.1) and (5.2). The Program Check Worksheet that we use is divided into three basic sections as shown in Figure 5.3. The left-hand side (the first three columns) is completed with information obtained from the static check calculations on the Analog Computer Worksheet. For this example these entries are self-explanatory. The middle section (columns 4 and 5) uses data from our scaling calculations. The normalizing constant symbols and magnitudes for each problem variable are entered as shown. Note that the forcing function in (5.1) is normalized by both the coefficient on $\bar{z}$ *and* by $\bar{z}_N$, hence we enter $2\bar{z}_N$ in column 4 in the lower part of the table. Then, in the upper part of the table, column 6 is the product of columns 2 and 4. In the lower part of the table, column 6 is the product of columns 2 and 5. Column 7 gives the descaled static check values, which we then substitute into the *original* unscaled equation. The entries in column 7 are the product of those in columns 3 and 5.

The substitution into the original equation and IC's is illustrated on the bottom half of the worksheet. Note the sign change for the descaled forcing function entry. This is done because the indirect programming procedure usually requires that we program the negative of our desired forcing function. We again change the sign to compensate for this fact.

Close numerical agreement in our final numerical reduction indicates that we have correctly magnitude-scaled the original equation and that we have made no errors in our static check calculations. Further, since the static check calculations depend on our flow diagram, we check this part of our programming also. We should normally expect slide-rule accuracy for the agreement across the equal sign. If we do not achieve an equality we should first go back and recheck our static check calculations, as an error there will certainly cause a failure of our program check. A neat and systematic approach to both checks usually ensures success.

| Lab _____ | | | Name | | |
|---|---|---|---|---|---|
| **PROGRAM CHECK WORKSHEET** | | | Date | | Sect. |
| | | | Course | | Prob. $Ex.\,5.2$ |

| From Static Check Sheet | | | From Scaling Calculations | | To be used in Program Check | |
|---|---|---|---|---|---|---|
| Amp. no. | Normalized variable symbol | Static check IC value | Normalizing constant symbol | Normalizing constant numerical value | Unscaled variable symbol | Variable's descaled static check value |
| $1$ | $\ddot{x}_{z_{\eta}}$ | $+0.900$ | $\dddot{z}_N$ | $50$ | $\dddot{z}$ | $+45.0$ |
| $5$ | $\ddot{x}_{y}$ | $-0.500$ | $\ddot{z}_N$ | $10$ | $\ddot{z}$ | $-5.0$ |
| $3$ | $\dot{x}_{z}$ | $+0.750$ | $\dot{z}_N$ | $10$ | $\dot{z}$ | $+7.5$ |
| $6$ | $x_{z}$ | $-0.100$ | $z_N$ | $10$ | $z$ | $-1.0$ |
| Amp. or pot no. | Programmed forcing function | Static check IC value | Normalization algebraic value | Normalization numerical value | Unscaled forcing function | Forcing function's descaled static check value |
| $P1$ | $-0.700u_{-1}(t)$ | $-0.700$ | $2\dddot{z}_N$ | $100$ | $-70u_{-1}(t)$ | $-70.0$ |
| | | | | | | |
| | | | | | | |
| | | | | | | |

$\qquad\qquad\qquad\qquad\qquad\qquad\qquad\qquad\qquad$ (Sign change)

Unscaled Equation: $\longrightarrow 2\dddot{z} + 10\ddot{z} + 6\dot{z} + 15z = 70u_{-1}(t)$

Substitution of Descaled
static check values: $\longrightarrow 2(+45.0) + 10(-5.0) + 6(+7.5) + 15(-1.0) \overset{?}{=} +70.0$

Numerical Reduction: $\longrightarrow +90.0 - 50.0 \quad +45.0 \quad -15.0 \overset{?}{=} +70.0$

$\qquad\qquad\qquad\qquad\qquad +135.0 \quad -65.0 \overset{?}{=} +70.0$

Equation Verification: $\longrightarrow +70.0 = +70.0$

Unscaled nonzero initial conditions: $\longrightarrow \ddot{z}(0) = -5.0 \qquad \dot{z}(0) = +7.5$

Substitution of descaled
static check values: $\longrightarrow -5.0 = -5.0 \qquad +7.5 = +7.5$

Nonzero IC verification: $\longrightarrow \checkmark \qquad\qquad \checkmark$

Figure 5.3

**5.3**
**summary** The static and program check procedures are designed strictly as an aid to the programmer. Computer operation should generally not be attempted until both checks have confirmed the correctness of the program. When these

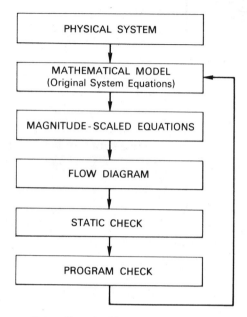

**Figure 5.4** *Problem-solving procedure*

checks are completed we "close the loop" on the problem-solving process, as shown diagrammatically in Figure 5.4. The work indicated by the blocks has then been verified.

## PROBLEMS

5.1. Starting with Equations (5.1) and (5.2) in Example 5.1, and using the normalizing constants given by (5.4), confirm the magnitude-scaled equation and initial conditions given on the Analog Computer Worksheet for this example.

5.2. Using the results of Problems 4.8 and 4.9, calculate a static check for the given system. In view of the fact that $\theta(0)=0$, what should be done to provide an initial condition on the integrator whose output is $-x_\theta$? Why?

5.3. Continue Problem 5.2 by calculating a program check for the given system. A confirmation of this check should indicate accurate scaling and flow-diagramming work. Because of the large numbers involved, do not expect accuracy better than about 1% on your program check.

5.4. Given an analog computer flow diagram wired as shown in Figure 5.5.

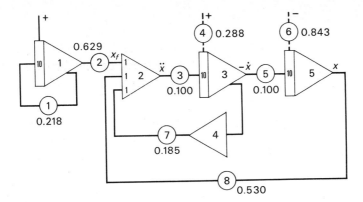

**Figure 5.5**

(a) Give the mathematical representation of the scaled forcing function $x_f$.

(b) Describe the initial conditions and give their values.

(c) Calculate the static check value for the output of amplifier 2.

5.5. How would the static check value for the output of A2 in Problem 5.4 change if the signs (computer reference input polarities) were changed on P4 and P6? Would this new value represent a valid static check? Why?

# chapter six

**6.0**
**introduction**
We have mentioned briefly the necessity for time scaling when we introduced the general concept of scaling in Section 4.0. We pointed out there that we would probably have to "speed up," or "slow down," most computer problems in order to bring the actual running time of the computer within acceptable limits. In linear system study, we usually like to obtain solutions to the kinds of problems with which we are concerned in about 100 seconds or less. Thus a problem involving space flight would have to be speeded up, whereas the phenomena occurring in, say, an electrical network might take place in such a short time that we would have to slow the computer down by several orders of magnitude. As a general rule of thumb, we time scale the computer such that we have no frequency components in the solution greater than 1 rad/sec.

As with magnitude scaling, there are several different techniques one can use in time scaling. One could make certain substitutions in the equations themselves in order to obtain equations written in terms of some new "computer time." However, our method involves time scaling the computer, not the equations. As a result, magnitude scaling and time scaling are "uncoupled" in our programming; we are thus able to alter one without changing the other. Time scaling the computer involves a very simple adjustment of the integrator gains; no other computing element is affected. We time scale the computer

# time scaling

after we have magnitude scaled the equations. In fact, the process of magnitude scaling clearly indicates the requirement for time scaling. As mentioned in Chapter 4, time scaling results in a very simple addition to the rule for the labeling of the time axis on recorder plots given by (3.13) in Section 3.2.

For an introductory treatment of the topic, we define either of the following situations to require time scaling:

(a) If the magnitude-scaling calculations of the given problem require that the integrator input pots, discussed in Section 4.1, be set to values significantly greater, or less, than unity.

(b) When we are required to generate a sinusoidal forcing function whose radian frequency is greater than about 1 rad/sec.

The first situation results when the ratios of normalizing constants in our magnitude scaling yield very large or very small numbers. This would occur for example, when $y_N \ll \dot{y}_N$, $\dot{y}_N \ll \ddot{y}_N$, etc. The second situation can be illustrated by referring to relation (3.17) together with the final flow diagram (Figure 3.13) shown for Example 3.5. If the forcing function's radian frequency $\omega$ is greater than 1 rad/sec, we would time scale the computer so as to reduce the gains on integrators A1 and A2 to values less than unity. We will see in the next section that the effect of time scaling is to divide each integrator input gain by a time scale factor. We assign a special symbol $n$ to this time scale factor. In the case of the sinusoidal generator mentioned above, we would simply divide each integrator input pot by $n$; thus, P2 and P3 in the final flow diagram for Example 3.5 (Figure 3.13) would be set to the value $\omega/n$. We would then choose the value of $n$ to be such that the pot setting would lie in the range between 0.100 and 1.00. For example, if we were programming a sinusoidal function, where $\omega$ was 377 rad/sec, and if we chose the time scale factor $n$ to be 500, we would have pot settings of 0.754.

The above discussion is developed more thoroughly in the following section where we formally consider the theory of time scaling and examine its effect on the linear computing elements.

## 6.1 definitions and example

We time scale the computer by considering the introduction of a new independent time variable, in order to be able to speed up, or slow down, our problem. The defining relation is

$$\tau = nt \tag{6.1}$$

where

$t$ = real time
$\tau$ = computer time
$n$ = time scale factor

Both time variables, $t$ and $\tau$, carry the same units. Thus, the time scale factor $n$ is a dimensionless quantity. It is, of course, a positive number, but it can be either greater, or less, than unity.

Now, we must consider the effect of the introduction of the new independent variable $\tau$ on the linear computing elements we discussed in Chapter 2. The potentiometer, since it simply multiplies a variable by a number less than unity, is clearly not affected by any change of the independent variable. Also, the coefficient, inverting, and summing amplifiers, although they may handle time-varying quantities, are likewise not affected by our change in time. The integrator, on the other hand, is affected by the substitution defined by (6.1). To see this, let us combine relations (4.17) and (4.21) and write

$$x_y = -\frac{\dot{y}_N}{y_N} \int \dot{x}_y \, dt \tag{6.2}$$

The ratio of the normalizing constants $\dot{y}_N/y_N$ came about as a result of the magnitude-scaling procedure. From (6.1) we have

$$dt = \frac{1}{n} \, d\tau \tag{6.3}$$

If we now write (6.2) in a more rigorous form, and use (6.3), we have

$$x_y = -\left[\frac{\dot{y}_N}{y_N} \int_0^t \dot{x}_y \left(\frac{1}{n} \, d\tau\right) - x_y(0)\right] \tag{6.4}$$

We now must integrate over the new interval 0 to $\tau$, since we have introduced a new independent variable. We now have as a defining relation for the time-scaled integrator,

$$x_y = -\left[\frac{\dot{y}_N}{ny_N}\int_0^\tau \dot{x}_y\, d\tau - x_y(0)\right] \tag{6.5}$$

The result indicated by (6.5) means that we have a program for our integrators as shown in Figure 6.1. The reader can compare this program with that shown

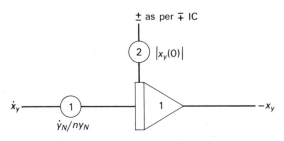

**Figure 6.1** *Time scaling of integrator*

in Figure 4.3, which showed the effect of magnitude scaling only. We note that the effect of time scaling our computer integrators is simply a new setting for our integrator input pots. The input potentiometers are set to the same ratio of normalizing constants as before, but now the ratio is divided by the time scale factor $n$. The computer now integrates in the new "$\tau$ time" and, since we are free to determine the constant of proportionality $n$ between $t$ and $\tau$, we can speed up, or slow down, the rate of integration. We say we have "time scaled the computer." By choosing $n$, we can obtain reasonable numbers for integrator input pot settings. This is the basis for statement (a) defining situations for time scaling in Section 6.0. As a general rule, we choose the value of $n$ so that the integrator gains are no greater than unity. Some general suggestions for the choice of convenient values for $n$ will be given in Section 6.3.

We illustrate the above theory of time scaling in Example 6.1, but first we summarize the general concept of time scaling in Table 6.1. As shown in

**Table 6.1** *Time-scaling Summary*

| If the original problem: | Then we choose: | Which has the effect of: |
| --- | --- | --- |
| Runs too fast | $n > 1$ | Slowing down the computer solution |
| Requires no time scaling | $n = 1$ | Running the problem in real time |
| Runs too slow | $n < 1$ | Speeding up the computer solution |

Figure 6.1, the effect of time scaling is to divide every integrator input pot in our program by the time scale factor $n$. This further explains the information contained in Table 6.1. For $n > 1$, we simply reduce the rate at which our

integrators operate, thereby slowing down the problem solution. For $n < 1$, the converse is true. We now apply time scaling to a specific numerical example.

### example 6.1

Consider the equation

$$\ddot{y} + 2.4\dot{y} + 144y = 0 \tag{6.6}$$

with

$$\dot{y}(0) = 54 \text{ ft/sec}$$
$$y(0) = 0$$

Assume that, based on an estimate of the maximum absolute values of the problem variables, we can choose

$$y_N = 5.0 \text{ ft}$$
$$\dot{y}_N = 62.5 \text{ ft/sec} \tag{6.7}$$
$$\ddot{y}_N = 750 \text{ ft/sec}^2$$

This would require integrator input pot settings of

$$\frac{\ddot{y}_N}{\dot{y}_N} = \frac{750}{62.5} = 12.0 \tag{6.8}$$

and

$$\frac{\dot{y}_N}{y_N} = \frac{62.5}{5.0} = 12.5 \tag{6.9}$$

We obviously cannot achieve such integrator gains. Thus, we have a clear requirement for time scaling, in accordance with Condition (a) of Section 6.0.

If we were to choose a time scale factor $n$ of 12.5, we would reduce the gains to 0.960 and 1.00, respectively. However, since we note that $\omega_n$, from (6.6), is 12 rad/sec, we should probably choose a slightly larger value for $n$. This is in keeping with Condition (b) of Section 6.0 regarding frequencies greater than 1 rad/sec. Furthermore, we will see in Section 6.3 that a choice of 12.5 is not too convenient in terms of interpreting our graphical results. Thus, we choose $n = 20$ in this example. With this value, (6.8) and (6.9) are

$$\frac{\ddot{y}_N}{n\dot{y}_N} = \frac{12.0}{20} = 0.600 \tag{6.10}$$

and

$$\frac{\dot{y}_N}{ny_N} = \frac{12.5}{20} = 0.625 \tag{6.11}$$

Using (6.7) with (6.6), the reader can confirm that the magnitude-scaled equation is

$$\ddot{x}_y + 0.200\dot{x}_y + 0.960x_y = 0 \tag{6.12}$$

with

$$\dot{x}_y(0) = 0.864$$

The flow diagram is as shown in Figure 6.2. The reader should patch and run this program. It is interesting to observe the effect of different time scale factors on the response, especially on the speed and accuracy of the plotting equipment used. One may wish to try the following

| $n$ | P1 | P3 |
|---|---|---|
| 20.0 | 0.600 | 0.625 |
| 12.5 | 0.960 | 1.000 |
| 2.5 | 4.800 | 5.000 |

The settings over 1.00 would obviously require gain 10's on A2 and A3. Most types of plotting equipment would yield degraded accuracies for $n = 5$ or lower.

Because we had $n > 1$ in the above example, we have slowed down the computer solution compared to real time. Even though we solved the problem in "$\tau$ time," we certainly want to label our results in real "$t$ time." We show a simple rule for doing this in the next section.

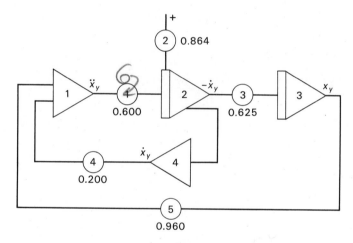

Figure 6.2

Based on the definition given in (6.1), we have

$$t = \frac{\tau}{n} \tag{6.13}$$

Therefore, since the computer operates in computer, or $\tau$, time, our graphical results would be in terms of $\tau$ along the horizontal, or time, axis. Since we are interested in presenting the results in real, or $t$, time, we see that we simply need to divide every time value by the time scale factor $n$. Thus, the rule we gave in relation (3.13) for one particular type of strip recorder is modified now for time-scaled problems to read

$$\text{Time (in seconds) at 1 in. mark} = \frac{60}{n \text{ (paper speed)}} \tag{6.14}$$

Strictly speaking, this really is not a modification at all, because (6.14) reduces to (3.13) for the nontime-scaled case, that is, $n = 1$.

The application of the above rule is illustrated in Figure 6.3, which is a plot of the response $y$ of (6.6) in Example 6.1. The paper speed was 3 in./min, with $n = 20$. Note the labeling of the vertical axis also. Since $y_N = 5.0$ ft, we have, as with Figure 4.7, the *value* $\pm 5.0$ at the $\pm 2\frac{1}{4}$ in. marks, respectively.

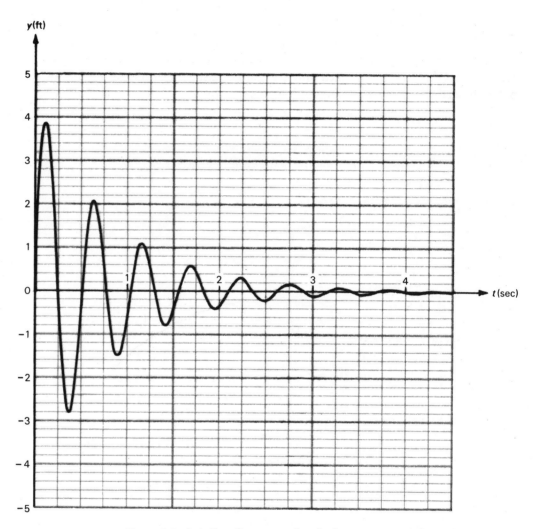

**Figure 6.3** *Labeling of computer plot, displacement y versus time t*

### 6.3 choice of time scale factor

The basic criterion for the choice of a time scale factor is the desire to make all integrator input gains about equal to or less than unity. Often this requires a certain trade-off in our choice of $n$, since obviously only one time scale factor can be selected in any given program. We choose a value for $n$ that is the best compromise for all the integrators in the problem.

The rule given by (6.14) should also be considered in choosing a time scale factor. We obviously try to choose a number such that the values of time at the major subdivisions (inch marks) on our graph paper are reasonable. For example, the value of $n = 20$ that we used in Example 6.1 is very good, especially when used with a paper speed of 3 in./min. The choice of $n = 12.5$, which we considered in that example, would have yielded awkward numbers (1.6, 3.2, etc.) at the inch marks.

**6.4**
**summary**

The discussion in this chapter has only covered the basics of time scaling. However, these basic principles, correctly applied in more sophisticated problems, will result in the successful time scaling of the computer. We again emphasize that the procedure we have outlined involves a scaling of the computer, not the equations. Because the techniques of magnitude and time scaling are essentially separate from each other, we can adjust either while on the computer. Indeed, the optimum magnitude-scaling constants and time scale factor are usually discovered by actually running the computer problem on the computer.

Finally, we list some important, but often missed, facts about time scaling that may not have been properly emphasized previously. They are

(a) *Every* integrator in the program is time scaled by the *same* time scale factor.
(b) The integrator IC's are *not* affected by our choice of $n$.
(c) It is very important to *record* the final value of $n$ used in the running of a problem. Special entries are reserved for $n$ in our Analog Computer Worksheets.
(d) Only integrator input pots are affected by the choice of $n$. (Pots such as P4 and P5 in the program for Example 6.1 are not affected.)
(e) Graphs are always labeled in *real* time, using the rule given in (6.14).
(f) Convenient numbers are chosen for $n$, so that the interpretation of our graphs does not become too complicated.

## PROBLEMS

6.1. As an illustration of the requirement for time scaling in an analog computer problem, consider the *RLC* series circuit shown in Figure 6.4, with typical element values as given.

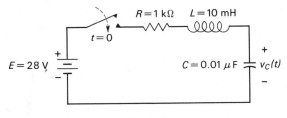

**Figure 6.4**

(a) Find the damping ratio $\zeta$ and the natural frequency $\omega_n$ of this circuit.
(b) Show that the expression for the voltage across the capacitor $v_C(t)$ is

$$v_C(t) = C_1 + C_2 e^{-\sigma t} \sin(\omega_d t + \phi)$$

Assume that the initial voltage across the capacitor is zero. $C_1$ and $C_2$ are constants.

(c) The result in part (b) indicates that the damped frequency of oscillation $\omega_d$ is quite large. Find the value of $\omega_d$ and, assuming that one wished to plot the analog computer solution of $v_C(t)$, suggest an appropriate value of the time scale factor $n$, which allows the solution to be sufficiently "slowed down" for most plotting equipment.

6.2. Discuss the effect of time scaling on the sine-cosine generator shown in the final program of Example 3.5. What pots would be affected, and what would be their new settings?

6.3. Confirm Equation (6.12) and its IC.

6.4. Assume a second-order differential equation is to be programmed in which the forcing function is

$$f(t) = 4 \sin 7\pi t$$

Further, assume the following normalizing constants have been chosen

$$\ddot{y}_N = 25, \qquad \dot{y}_N = 6.25, \qquad y_N = 1$$

Select a time scale factor, and give a justification for the value chosen.

6.5. The equation

$$\ddot{z} + A\dot{z} + Bz = 0$$
$$\dot{z}(0) = 0$$
$$z(0) = C$$

is magnitude scaled to give

$$\ddot{x}_z + 0.1A\dot{x}_z + 0.025Bx_z = 0$$
$$x_z(0) = 0.4C$$

The flow diagram is as shown in Figure 6.5.

(a) Find the normalizing constants $\ddot{z}_N$, $\dot{z}_N$, and $z_N$ used to magnitude scale this equation.

$$\ddot{z}_N \to , \ 1A = \frac{A\dot{z}_N}{\ddot{z}_N} = \frac{1}{10} \qquad \dot{z}_N = 10$$

$$\ddot{z}_N = 10 \times 10 = \underline{100}$$

$$z_N = 0.25 \times 100 = 2.5$$

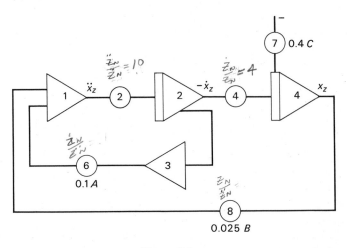

Figure 6.5

(b) Calculate the settings of pots 2 and 4, assuming no time scaling.

(c) Choose an appropriate time scale factor $n$.

(d) As a result of your choice of $n$, which pot settings change, and what are their new settings?

6.6. In examining the effect of time scaling on an integrator, the use of the defining relation (6.1) resulted in Equation (6.4). The upper limit of integration was then changed to $\tau$ (not $\tau/n$, as might be suggested by Equation (6.1)). Explain this seeming incongruity.

6.7. Consider the plot of the response shown in Figure 4.7, Section 4.4. If the computer was time scaled by $n > 1$, would the point of maximum displacement move to the left or to the right on the graph paper, or would it stay in the same place? Why? (Assume the plotter paper speed was not changed.)

6.8. A linear first-order system, with zero initial conditions, is defined by the constant coefficient differential equation

$$\dot{y} + \frac{1}{\tau} y = A u_{-1}(t)$$

$\tau$ is the time constant and $A$ is the magnitude of the step function input.

(a) It is easy to show that the maximum magnitudes of the variables are

$$|y|_{max} = A\tau, \qquad |\dot{y}|_{max} = A$$

If the smallest permissible normalizing constants are chosen, what is the setting of the integrator input pot?

(b) For the case above, what should be the relation between the system time constant $\tau$ and the time scale factor $n$ for unity integrator gain?

6.9. Extend the results of Problem 6.8 to the system of Figure 6.6 that represents the idealized mechanical model of a motor load. Let

$T(t)$ = applied torque = $100\pi u_{-1}(t)$ ft-lb
$J$ = moment of inertia = 0.035 ft-lb-sec²/rad
$B$ = rotational damping constant = 0.5 ft-lb-sec/rad
$\omega$ = reference direction for angular velocity

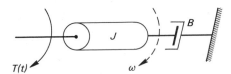

Figure 6.6

(a) Write the differential equation for this system, assuming $\omega(0) = 0$. Put in the numbers.

(b) Choose reasonable values for $\omega_N$ and $\dot{\omega}_N$ and magnitude scale the equation.

(c) Choose a reasonable value for the time scale factor $n$.

(d) Develop the complete analog flow diagram.

6.10. Consider the $RC$ circuit shown in Figure 4.1, Section 4.0. Choose appropriate normalizing constants $\dot{q}_N$ and $q_N$ and a time scale factor. What would be the resulting integrator input pot setting?

# chapter seven

**7.0 introduction**  In all our previous examples involving magnitude scaling, we have selected normalizing constants based on an assumed a priori knowledge of the maximum absolute values of the problem variables. In this chapter we introduce several techniques used to obtain estimates of the maximum values. We want to emphasize the word *estimates*; an exact procedure is, in general, not available and, since we choose our normalizing constants larger anyway, an exact knowledge of the maxima for a given problem is not required. Normally, we would like to establish the maximum expected value of the dependent variable and its derivatives in order to prevent amplifier overloads.

If our estimated maxima are too conservative (larger than the actual maxima), we will pick normalizing constants larger than necessary. We saw in Section 4.2 that this would result in very small values for the normalized variables appearing at the amplifier outputs. However, this situation can easily be corrected by the magnitude rescaling procedure discussed in Section 4.2. If we have poor estimates for maxima (too low), we will probably choose normalizing constants too small and, as a result, we will have amplifier overloads. If several amplifiers overload in a problem, and especially if these overloads occur very quickly, it may be difficult to isolate the true cause and determine the proper corrective action. We can rather easily make the necessary

# estimation of maximum values of problem variables

corrections if our estimates are large by a factor of perhaps as much as 10, but if our estimates are low by that amount we may have a great deal of trouble making our program run. The point to be made is that we seek intelligent estimates of variable maxima, based on good engineering judgement. If the normalizing constants that we then choose are not optimum we can refine them after a trial computer run. In any problem of reasonable complexity this is almost always required.

In the next section we will tabulate some guidelines for the estimation of maximum values based on linear system theory. We will list expressions that can be used to calculate maximum values of the dependent variable and its derivatives for certain special cases involving simple first- and second-order systems. By analogy with these special cases, we can then estimate maxima for some classes of equations. In Section 7.2 we will introduce the "equal coefficient rule," which can be used for higher-order equations and/or non-linear or nonconstant-coefficient equations where linear system guidance fails. We will illustrate both of these techniques with an example.

Probably the most straightforward method of estimating maxima is based on a knowledge of the physical system itself. For instance, in a mechanical problem such as shown in Example 3.1, we may have some knowledge of the maximum possible displacement of the mass. This may be known based on the physical constraints in the original system. (Perhaps as in an automobile suspension system, where the wheel travel is obviously constrained to a certain range.) We can choose a normalizing constant for the dependent variable based on this known absolute maximum. The remaining normalizing constants can be chosen based on other known constraints or, as will be further explained in Section 7.2, they can be chosen so as to form a monotonic set, where successive values differ by an amount about equal to the system natural frequency.

### 7.1 linear system guidance

Most systems of interest in linear system study can be described by first- or second-order, constant- coefficient differential equations. The maxima occurring in such equations are, in general, well-defined and can be calculated (at least for certain cases of damping) by classical maximization techniques. If one has such a list of maxima available for the dependent variable and its derivatives then the maximum values in any equation can be estimated, even though the actual damping present may be different from the special cases for which the values are known exactly.

A tabulated list of maxima for simple linear equations is available and has been included in Table 7.1. The entries in this table are not derived here;

**Table 7.1**  *Maximum Values For Linear Systems*

| System Equations and IC's | Conditions | $|y|_{max}$ | $|\dot{y}|_{max}$ | $|\ddot{y}|_{max}$ |
|---|---|---|---|---|
| *First-order systems* | | | | |
| $\dot{y} + \alpha y = Au_{-1}(t)$ $\quad y(0) = 0$ | $\alpha > 0$ | $\dfrac{A}{\alpha}$ | $A$ | ... |
| $\dot{y} + \alpha y = 0$ $\quad y(0) = A$ | $\alpha > 0$ | $A$ | $\alpha A$ | ... |
| *Second-order systems* | | | | |
| $\ddot{y} + 2\zeta\omega_n\dot{y} + \omega_n^2 y = Au_{-1}(t)$ $\quad y(0) = 0, \dot{y}(0) = 0$ | $\zeta = 0$ | $\dfrac{2A}{\omega_n^2}$ | $\dfrac{A}{\omega_n}$ | $A$ |
| $\ddot{y} + 2\zeta\omega_n\dot{y} + \omega_n^2 y = Au_{-1}(t)$ $\quad y(0) = 0, \dot{y}(0) = 0$ | $\zeta = 1$ | $\dfrac{A}{\omega_n^2}$ | $\dfrac{A}{\omega_n e^{a}}$ | $A$ |
| $\ddot{y} + 2\zeta\omega_n\dot{y} + \omega_n^2 y = 0$ $\quad y(0) = 0, \dot{y}(0) = A$ | $\zeta = 0$ | $\dfrac{A}{\omega_n}$ | $A$ | $\omega_n A$ |
| $\ddot{y} + 2\zeta\omega_n\dot{y} + \omega_n^2 y = 0$ $\quad y(0) = A, \dot{y}(0) = 0$ | $\zeta \geqq 0$ | $A$ | $A\omega_n$ (for $\zeta = 0$) $\dfrac{A\omega_n}{e}$ (for $\zeta = 1$) | $\omega_n^2 A$ |
| $\ddot{y} + 2\zeta\omega_n\dot{y} + \omega_n^2 y = 0$ $\quad y(0) = 0, \dot{y}(0) = A$ | $\zeta = 1$ | $\dfrac{A}{\omega_n e}$ | $A$ | $2\omega_n A$ |

a $e$ denotes the base of the natural, or Naperian, logarithms; that is, 2.718. . . .

the interested reader is encouraged to verify the maxima listed using classical maximization techniques. Some entries are self-explanatory, such as those for the first-order cases. The second-order cases are derived for damping ratios $\zeta$ of either 0 or 1. Since, in general, no real physical system experiences either such damping ratio, we use the case that is the best compromise for the given problem. In some cases ($\zeta$ of 0.500, for example), one might consider calculating the maxima for $\zeta = 0$ and $\zeta = 1$ and then using the most conservative (largest) estimate.

We note from Table 7.1 that maxima are calculated for either step inputs or initial conditions on one derivative. Since we are dealing with linear systems, the principle of superposition holds so that we could, by simply adding the values due to each cause, estimate maxima for both a forcing function *and* IC (or IC's). For instance, again referring to Example 3.1, we could estimate maxima due to the step function input given in (3.4) and also the IC given in (3.5). If we summed the estimates due to these two causes we would be assured that the actual maxima would not exceed our estimates. Usually, we would obtain a very conservative estimate of maxima, especially on the higher-order terms.

We illustrate the use of Table 7.1 in Example 7.1. The reader should note that the absolute value of $A$ in Table 7.1 is used for all calculations.

### example 7.1

For this example we return to (6.6) in Example 6.1 and estimate maxima for $y$, $\dot{y}$, and $\ddot{y}$. We had

$$\ddot{y} + 2.4\dot{y} + 144y = 0 \tag{7.1}$$

with

$$\begin{aligned}\dot{y}(0) &= 54 \text{ ft/sec} \\ y(0) &= 0\end{aligned} \tag{7.2}$$

We see from (7.1) that $\zeta = 0.1$ and $\omega_n = 12$ rad/sec. Since we have no entry in Table 7.1 for $\zeta = 0.1$, we use the $\zeta = 0$ case, with no forcing function and an IC on velocity only. Thus, the entries we use to estimate maxima are those given as the third entry under the Second-order systems' section of Table 7.1. From the table, we have

$$\begin{aligned}|y|_{\max} &= \frac{A}{\omega_n} = \frac{54}{12} = 4.5 \text{ ft} \\[2mm] |\dot{y}|_{\max} &= A = 54 \text{ ft/sec} \\[2mm] |\ddot{y}|_{\max} &= \omega_n A = (12)(54) = 648 \text{ ft/sec}^2\end{aligned} \tag{7.3}$$

Based on these estimates, we are able to choose the set of normalizing constants given in (6.7). If the student runs the program for Example 6.1, the following true maxima should be observed:

$$\begin{aligned}|y|_{\max} &= 3.88 \text{ ft} \\ |\dot{y}|_{\max} &= 53.8 \text{ ft/sec} \\ |\ddot{y}|_{\max} &= 577 \text{ ft/sec}^2\end{aligned} \tag{7.4}$$

Comparing these actual maxima with those estimated in (7.3), we note that either set of values would probably suggest the same set of normalizing constants as was used. This emphasizes our comments made in Section 7.0 regarding the estimation of maximum values. Because we choose our normalizing constants to be the next larger "good" number anyway, we do not need an exact estimate of maxima. Most applications involving Table 7.1 do not yield results as good as in the above simple example. However, the table yields upper limits that allow one to "get on the computer" and refine his estimates.

### 7.2 equal coefficient rule

For higher-order systems, we can estimate maximum values using an equal coefficient rule. Although this rule is not really applicable to nonlinear and/or nonconstant-coefficient equations, it also provides some help in the scaling of such systems. We simply state the equal coefficient rule and illustrate its application with a comprehensive example. A formal "proof" of the rule is not given here. The equal coefficient rule is:

> For stable, linear, homogeneous differential equations, the maximum value of the dependent variable and its derivatives may be estimated by selecting values for the maxima that cause the coefficients in the final scaled equation to be approximately equal. For nonhomogeneous equations with zero IC's the values are selected such that the coefficient on the zeroth-order term is approximately twice that of the others.

The actual coefficients in the final scaled equation depend upon the choice of normalizing constants, and these depend, of course, upon the maximum values of the variables. Hence, to discover maxima using the equal coefficient rule, we modify the multiply-and-divide procedure introduced in Chapter 4 and illustrated in Equations (4.34) through (4.40). We make the tacit assumption that the maximum value is identically equal to its associated normalizing constant, thereby allowing multiplication by the former and division by the latter. Thus, the final coefficients may be expressed in terms of the desired maximum values. We illustrate the application of this rule in Example 7.2.

The equal coefficient rule is valid if the normalizing constants chosen from the calculated maximum values form a monotonic set; that is, the values should continually increase or decrease for each derivative in turn. This is not to say that several of the normalizing constants can not be equal in magnitude; the general trend must simply be toward larger, or smaller, values. Some feeling for this restriction may be obtained if we consider most solutions to typical differential equations as containing sinusoidally varying components. We know successive derivatives of the sine function introduce successively higher powers of the radian frequency $\omega$. Thus, we should expect the maximum values of successive derivatives to form a monotonic set. When using the equal coefficient rule we can often throw out a "bad" term that may result and replace it with one that allows the entire set to be monotonic. This property of monotonicity (by a factor of $\omega_n$) in real physical systems is the basis for our statement in Section 7.0 regarding estimation of maximum values when the physical constraints of the problem may only suggest a maximum for *one* of the orders of derivatives. As a gross "ballpark" figure, we can estimate maxima for the higher and/or lower orders of derivatives of the dependent variable by assuming a difference of about $\omega_n$ between successive terms. The actual mechanics of applying the equal coefficient rule are illustrated in the following example.

### example 7.2

In this example we use the equal coefficient rule to estimate maxima for the third-order system described by (5.1) and (5.2) in Example 5.1. We had there

$$2\dddot{z} + 10\ddot{z} + 6\dot{z} + 15z = 70u_{-1}(t) \tag{7.5}$$

with

$$\begin{aligned} \ddot{z}(0) &= -5.0 \text{ m/sec}^2 \\ \dot{z}(0) &= +7.5 \text{ m/sec} \\ z(0) &= 0 \end{aligned} \tag{7.6}$$

Even though we do not have all zero initial conditions we, in accordance with the equal coefficient rule for nonhomogeneous equations, select our maxima such that the zeroth-order coefficient is about twice the others. We follow the procedure described previously. For convenience in notation, we use a subscript $m$ on a variable to mean the maximum absolute value. From (7.5) we have

$$2\dddot{z}_m \left(\frac{\dddot{z}}{\dddot{z}_N}\right) + 10\ddot{z}_m \left(\frac{\ddot{z}}{\ddot{z}_N}\right) + 6\dot{z}_m \left(\frac{\dot{z}}{\dot{z}_N}\right) + 15z_m \left(\frac{z}{z_N}\right) = 70u_{-1}(t) \tag{7.7}$$

This reduces to

$$\ddot{x}_z + \left(\frac{5\ddot{z}_m}{\dddot{z}_m}\right)\ddot{x}_z + \left(\frac{3\dot{z}_m}{\dddot{z}_m}\right)\dot{x}_z + \left(\frac{7.5z_m}{\dddot{z}_m}\right)x_z = \left(\frac{35}{\dddot{z}_m}\right)u_{-1}(t) \tag{7.8}$$

Now, the point of the equal coefficient rule is to make all the coefficients equal, except for the coefficient on $x_z$, which is to be twice the others. We make the other coefficients unity. This requires

$$\frac{35}{\dddot{z}_m} = 1 \quad \Rightarrow \dddot{z}_m \triangleq |\dddot{z}|_{\text{max}} = 35 \text{ m/sec}^3 \tag{7.9}$$

$$\frac{5\ddot{z}_m}{\dddot{z}_m} = 1 \quad \Rightarrow \ddot{z}_m \triangleq |\ddot{z}|_{\text{max}} = 7.0 \text{ m/sec}^2 \tag{7.10}$$

$$\frac{3\dot{z}_m}{\dddot{z}_m} = 1 \quad \Rightarrow \dot{z}_m \triangleq |\dot{z}|_{\text{max}} = 11.7 \text{ m/sec} \tag{7.11}$$

$$\frac{7.5z_m}{\dddot{z}_m} = 2 \Rightarrow z_m \triangleq |z|_{\text{max}} = 9.3 \text{ m} \tag{7.12}$$

These maxima do not form a monotonic set, so we might consider adjusting the magnitude of $|\ddot{z}|_{\text{max}}$ upward to cause it to lie between 11.7 and 35.0. If we did this, and if we then chose normalizing constants based on our maxima, we could choose the set

$$\dddot{z}_N = 50 \text{ m/sec}^3$$
$$\ddot{z}_N = 25 \text{ m/sec}^2$$
$$\dot{z}_N = 15 \text{ m/sec}$$
$$z_N = 10 \text{ m}$$

(7.13)

This is a perfectly acceptable set of constants, even though two are higher than the ones listed in (5.4) which were used to scale the equation. We might make some downward adjustments by rescaling, after a trial computer run. If the reader has run Example 5.1, the following actual maxima should have been observed:

$$|\dddot{z}|_{max} = 37.3 \text{ m/sec}^3$$
$$|\ddot{z}|_{max} = 7.0 \text{ m/sec}^2$$
$$|\dot{z}|_{max} = 7.5 \text{ m/sec}$$
$$|z|_{max} = 8.8 \text{ m}$$

(7.14)

We may conclude from the above results that the ECR has provided a simple, and reasonably accurate estimate for the maxima in our problem. While this may not always be the case, it is a very useful tool for the estimation of maximum values.

**7.3
summary**
The discussion and examples in this chapter have illustrated two techniques for the estimation of maximum values in our problems. Along with our knowledge of the original physical system, these techniques should allow the estimation of maxima for any problem in linear system theory. We again emphasize that we only require gross estimates of the maxima; if there is doubt as to a maximum we can choose a large conservative value and then, using the double-and-halve rule discussed in Section 4.2, we can optimize our magnitude scaling on the computer.

**PROBLEMS**

7.1. Confirm the values given for the maximum absolute values of $y$ and $\dot{y}$ in part (a) of Problem 6.8.

7.2. Use the equal coefficient rule to estimate maximum values for the system described by the third-order differential equation of Problem 4.8. Follow the procedure of Example 7.2. Based on your estimates, do the normalizing constants given in Problem 4.8 seem reasonable?

7.3. Consider the function, given in Problem 3.14, $x_f = At^2 e^{-\alpha t}$. Find the maximum values of $x_f$, $\dot{x}_f$, and $\ddot{x}_f$. Find the points in time at which these maxima occur.

7.4. Confirm the values given for $|y|_{max}$, $|\dot{y}|_{max}$, and $|\ddot{y}|_{max}$ for the first entry under the Second-order systems' section of Table 7.1; that is, for the system described by

$$\ddot{y} + \omega_n^2 y = A u_{-1}(t), \qquad y(0) = 0, \qquad \dot{y}(0) = 0$$

You should discover that these maxima occur at points in time of $\pi/\omega_n$, $\pi/2\omega_n$, and 0, respectively.

7.5. Consider the series $RLC$ electrical circuit shown in Problem 6.1, with

$$E = 1000 \text{ V}, \qquad L = 0.1 \text{ H}, \qquad R = 5 \ \Omega, \qquad C = 100 \ \mu\text{F}$$

Assume all initial conditions are zero and write a second-order differential equation in terms of charge $q$. Use the equal coefficient rule to estimate maximum values for $\ddot{q}$, $\dot{q}$, and $q$.

7.6. Estimate the maximum values for $\ddot{z}$, $\dot{z}$, and $z$ in

$$2\ddot{z} + 1.2\dot{z} + 18z = 0$$

where $z(0) = 5$ and $\dot{z}(0) = 0$.

7.7. Consider the third-order equation, where all initial conditions are zero,

$$\dddot{R} + 2\ddot{R} + 4\dot{R} + 40R = 100u_{-1}(t)$$

Use the equal coefficient rule to establish a set of normalizing constants. Do your results indicate a need for time scaling?

7.8. Given the differential equation, with initial conditions

$$\ddot{y} + \dot{y} + 25y = 25u_{-1}(t), \qquad y(0) = 0, \qquad \dot{y}(0) = 10$$

Use the information contained in Table 7.1 to estimate maximum values for $\ddot{y}$, $\dot{y}$, and $y$.

7.9. A second-order system, subject to a sinusoidal input, is described as follows, where all IC's are zero:

$$\ddot{y} + 8\dot{y} + 400y = 200 \cos 18.82t$$

Estimate maximum values for the dependent variable and its derivatives. (*Hint:* Review the concept of frequency response in any text on linear system theory and use the magnitude of the frequency response function, $G(j\omega)$, or normalized response curves, to find $|y|_{max}$. Then, use the equal coefficient rule.)

7.10. A second-order system, subject to an impulse input, is described as follows, where all IC's are zero:

$$\ddot{\theta} + 18.50\dot{\theta} + 5300\theta = 28{,}850u_0(t)$$

Estimate maximum values for the dependent variable and its derivatives. (*Hint:* The handling of an impulse forcing function was discussed in Example 3.8, but such functions can frequently be closely approximated by rapidly decaying exponentials. Assuming, from energy considerations, that $Au_0(t)$ could be approximated by some $Be^{-\alpha t}$ function having equal area, then, knowing $\alpha$, $B$ would be specified. Knowing $B$ would allow the use of Table 7.1, assuming $Be^{-\alpha t}$ could be treated as $Bu_{-1}(t)$. Try this idea using an $\alpha$ of 2.18.)

**problems**

# chapter eight

Thus far we have considered only linear, constant-coefficient differential equations to define the mathematical models of real physical systems. Often, however, even the simplest system will have such obvious nonlinearities that simple linear equations will not do. Common examples include such phenomena as rectification and filtering in electrical systems, physical constraints such as backlash in mechanical systems, "hammer" in fluid systems, etc. The reader may be familiar with so-called piecewise-linear methods of analysis, whereby the nonlinear aspects of systems are handled by linear approximations over arbitrarily small regions, or "pieces," of the entire dynamic range of operation. We can, for instance, analyze amplifier circuits by defining different models for certain frequency ranges of interest. The obvious result of such a technique is to yield several different mathematical models for any given system, each valid over a given interval. The equations associated with these separate models can be solved, yielding a set of solutions that define the response over any arbitrary interval of interest.

In order to handle systems containing simple nonlinearities on an analog computer it is desirable to have the ability to model the nonlinearity in terms of a so-called transfer characteristic, which is a graphical relation between the input and output. If the transfer characteristic can be successfully generated,

# transfer characteristics

then it can simply be inserted in the program at the appropriate point to describe an output as some nonlinear function of an input. For instance, if the spring force in a mechanical system were given by

$$F = Kx|x| \tag{8.1}$$

instead of by the familiar linear

$$F = Kx \tag{8.2}$$

then we could easily solve the problem if we could generate a transfer characteristic that has an output $F = Kx|x|$ for some given input $x$. The transfer characteristic would be as shown in Figure 8.1.

Since the desired output, in general, appears at the output of some amplifier, we must scale the transfer characteristic just as we would scale any other term in our equation. We use the concept of normalized variables, discussed in Chapter 4, to do this. Before considering normalization, however, we discuss the use of idealized diodes in analog computer circuits to generate transfer characteristics. Other techniques and components are available for generating transfer characteristics but, for this introductory treatment, we consider only the use of solid state diodes.

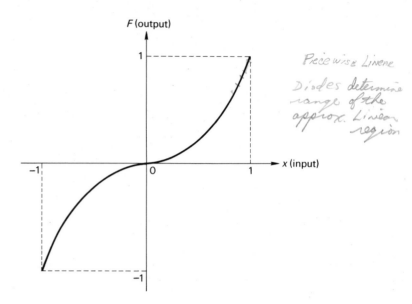

*Piecewise Linene*

*Diodes determine range of the approx. Linien region*

**Figure 8.1** *Transfer characteristic for* $F = Kx|x|$

**8.1 idealized diodes**

Computer mechanization of nonlinear mathematical models requires the use of some type of switching device so that arbitrary transfer characteristics can be generated. For instance, the characteristic shown in Figure 8.1 would require the use of some type of device exhibiting a square-law characteristic. Depending upon the accuracy required, such a nonlinear characteristic could be approximated by a series of linear "pieces," where each piece or segment could be obtained using some type of diode network. Many analog computers have installed devices called variable diode function generators (VDFG) for generation of arbitrary transfer characteristics. In this section, we discuss the ideal diode so that we can use it in simple applications for the generation of some common nonlinearities frequently encountered in systems analysis.

The generalized volt–ampere characteristic of a common germanium or silicon diode is shown in Figure 8.2. The point at which current begins to flow in any appreciable amount is typically of the order of a few tenths of a volt. For larger positive voltages, current flow increases very rapidly. Conversely,

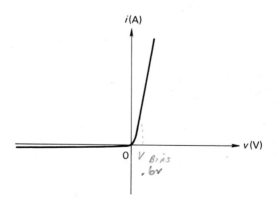

*V BIAS .6v*

**Figure 8.2** *Diode volt–ampere characteristic*

for negative applied voltage, only negligible current flow takes place. Thus we can say that the diode has a very large back, or reverse, resistance and a very low forward resistance.

For purposes of analysis, we wish to consider the diode as a simple *switch*; that is, as a device having infinite reverse resistance and zero forward resistance. Such a device is called an *ideal diode*. Its volt–ampere characteristic is as shown in Figure 8.3. We note that it is simply an idealization of the true characteristic

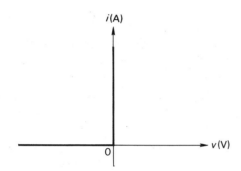

**Figure 8.3**  *Ideal diode volt–ampere characteristic*

shown in Figure 8.2. We assume the ideal diode conducts current with zero resistance for any applied voltage greater than zero. The idealized characteristic shown in Figure 8.3 is clearly the same as that of a perfect on–off switch. Such a device, combined with the high-gain amplifier discussed in Section 2.2, can be used in various configurations to generate arbitrary transfer characteristics. We analyze several such circuits in the next section. Before doing so, however, it is useful to establish a convenient flow diagram symbol for the ideal diode.

We use for the flow diagram symbol of an ideal diode the configuration shown in Figure 8.4. The notation of Figure 8.4 is more clearly understood

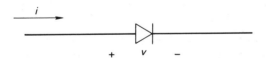

**Figure 8.4**  *Flow diagram symbol for diode*

if we think of the switching action of an ideal diode as follows:

> If the voltage across the ideal diode (due to the external circuit) is such as to force a current through the diode *in the direction of the arrow*, then the switch closes and a short circuit (zero resistance) is created.

In other words, we say the diode is either "forward-biased" (in which case the switch closes), or it is "reverse-biased" (this means it acts as an infinite resistance open circuit). These concepts are very important when we consider the use of the diode in various circuit configurations, which is done in the next section.

**8.2**
**diode circuits**

It would be nearly impossible to attempt to develop all the diode circuits necessary to represent the various nonlinear phenomena that commonly occur in nature. However, once some basic analysis techniques are developed it is reasonably easy to extend the analysis to more sophisticated circuits. In this section we discuss, through examples, several basic circuits showing the application of ideal diodes in transfer characteristic simulation. The reader should then be able to analyze most common diode circuits he may later encounter or require.

It must be emphasized at this point that circuits based on diodes that are assumed to have the ideal characteristic shown in Figure 8.3 are *not* precise. This means that the breakpoints and slopes of the desired transfer characteristics are not perfect. This may not be too severe in some simple applications (especially when using 100-V computers), but it is generally undesirable. This situation can be overcome by using *precision* circuits. Such circuits are specially designed to compensate for the slight forward voltage that must be present in a real diode in order for conduction to take place. We analyze several simple *ideal diode* circuits in the following examples, in order to emphasize introductory analytical techniques, but the reader is referred to Appendix B for a compilation of *precision* circuits. These precision circuits should be used for any actual computation. In fact, a useful exercise for the reader might be to wire both ideal and precision circuits and to examine the differences between them.

*example 8.1*

For this first example of an ideal diode circuit we analyze a nonprecise, halfwave rectifier. This is simply an operational amplifier whose output is held ("clamped") at zero for all inputs of one particular sign (polarity). For all inputs of the opposite polarity the circuit operates as a simple inverter. The circuit is as shown in Figure 8.5. The reader may wish to review the notation and development in Sections 2.2 and 2.3 in order to understand better this diode circuit. The point marked SJ is called the summing junction and is essentially the input point to the base of the first stage. Note that the ideal diode notation of Figure 8.4 has been used for the diode in the feedback loop. In accordance with the analogy drawn between the ideal diode and a perfect switch, we see that the diode effectively places either zero resistance or infinite resistance in parallel with the resistance $R_f$.

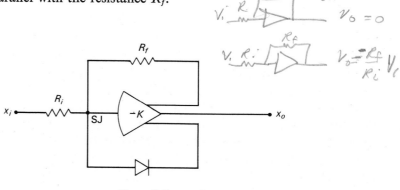

Figure 8.5

To develop the transfer characteristic (that is, the relation between the input $x_i$ and the output $x_o$) of this simple diode circuit, one only needs to consider the two possible polarities of the input, and the resulting output in each case. This is a general procedure that works for any other diode circuit we may encounter. For *positive* inputs $+x_i$, the output, if there is one, would tend to go negative because of the inversion in the high-gain amplifier. However, a negative output would result in a polarity across the diode as shown in Figure 8.4. This is true because the summing junction is a "virtual ground," as was pointed out in Section 2.2, and we have postulated that the output is at least *tending* toward a negative polarity for all positive inputs. Thus the diode is forward-biased, the "switch" closes, and a resultant short circuit appears around the high gain amplifier. This "shorts out" the amplifier and no amplification takes place. Therefore, for all positive inputs, the output is zero (it is said to be "clamped" at zero). For all *negative* inputs, the output, if there is one, would tend to go positive. Because SJ remains at essentially zero potential, the diode is then always reverse-biased, the "switch" never closes, and the only resistance in the feedback path is due to the normal feedback resistor $R_f$. This results in a device exactly like the one in Section 2.3, for which the relation between input and output is, in accordance with (2.10), given by

$$x_o = -\left(\frac{R_f}{R_i}\right) x_i \qquad (8.3)$$

If we consider, for convenience, the case where $R_f$ equals $R_i$, we see that, for all negative inputs, the device functions as a simple gain 1, inverting amplifier.

The net result of the above analysis may now be shown by considering the transfer characteristic (Figure 8.6). An operational amplifier with such a

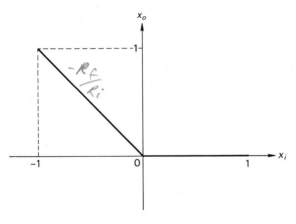

**Figure 8.6**

transfer characteristic obviously functions as a halfwave rectifier. All positive-going portions of the input result in zero output whereas all negative-going portions appear at the output with no change except a simple sign inversion. Such a device can thus be used to simulate many phenomena that commonly are encountered in systems analysis. If the diode is reversed in the circuit of this example the reader should confirm that the transfer characteristic would be such as to indicate zero output for all *negative* inputs and gain 1 (but inverted) outputs for all *positive* inputs.

It should again be emphasized at this point that the circuit of the above example is not precise, due to the nonideal nature of any real diode. Precision circuits for halfway rectifiers, and other nonlinearities, are shown in Appendix B. The reader can analyze these precision circuits in a manner very similar to the method discussed in Example 8.1 in order to show that they are more precise devices.

Another major class of diode circuits has been developed in order to represent situations in which one seeks an output that only increases to a certain given value no matter how large the input may become. These are many times referred to as various types of "limiter" circuits. Such a device might be of use, for example, in simulating a servomechanism whose output is prevented from exceeding certain limits due to physical constraints. In electrical problems, a limiter circuit could be used to represent certain classes of amplification. We analyze a very simple limiter circuit in Example 8.2.

### example 8.2

As another example of a nonprecise idealized diode circuit, consider an operational amplifier connected as shown in Figure 8.7. This circuit illustrates the

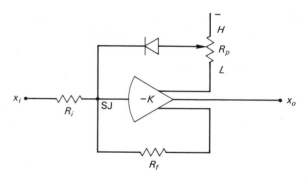

Figure 8.7

use of a potentiometer connected in a new configuration. Up to this point we have always connected pots in the manner discussed in Section 2.1; namely, with the output connected to an amplifier input directly and with the bottom, or "low," end grounded. In the diode circuit shown in Figure 8.7 we must connect the pot output (wiper arm) to a diode, with the low end connected to an amplifier output. Most computers have such "ungrounded" pots available or, as explained in Section A.3, some coefficient pots may be ungrounded by removing certain patchboard plugs. The input to the pot $R_p$ in the diode circuit of this example is taken from negative computer reference in the usual fashion. The $H$ and $L$ refer to the high and low ends, respectively, of the pot $R_p$.

To analyze this circuit in terms of the transfer characteristic, first consider the case of *positive* inputs. The output, if there is one, would be negative. This would result in both ends of $R_p$ having negative polarity, so that certainly the diode would be reverse-biased no matter where the wiper arm was set. The switch would therefore remain open and the circuit would function as a simple gain 1 inverter, if $R_f$ again equals $R_i$. The output would thus be the same as the input, except inverted, for all positive inputs.

For *negative* inputs the situation is slightly more complicated. Consider first the case where a very small negative input results in a very small positive output. Since negative reference is connected to the high end of $R_p$, the net polarity at the wiper arm is, for any reasonable pot setting, also negative for small positive outputs. However, as larger negative inputs to the amplifier cause larger positive outputs, the wiper arm, at some point, goes from negative to positive polarity. When this happens, the diode is forward-biased, the switch closes, and the amplifier has its output clamped at the value that caused the wiper arm to change polarity. This value depends upon the setting of $R_p$. Because of the manner in which $R_p$ is connected it cannot be set in the usual manner. Instead, it is simply adjusted until the desired limiting value is achieved. This is done by observing the output of the amplifier on the voltmeter for some reasonably large negative input.

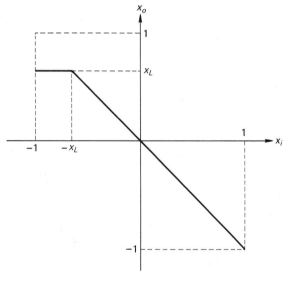

**Figure 8.8**

The resulting transfer characteristic of the limiter is then as shown in Figure 8.8. This is a so-called "single side" limiter because no limiting takes place for positive inputs. It can be shown that the setting $K$ of pot $R_p$ is related to the limited output value $x_L$ through the approximate relation

$$K = \frac{x_L}{1 + x_L} \tag{8.4}$$

This relation can be used to establish a starting point for the desired limiting on those computers having calibrated pots. In any case, the final adjustment is always made by observing the desired output.

The reader should be able to extend the above analysis to show that limiting in the "fourth-quadrant" occurs if the diode is reversed and if the input to

$R_p$ is changed from negative to positive reference. Furthermore, if two feed-back diode paths are used, one as shown in the example and the other as just described, then a full limiter results where both negative *and* positive outputs are limited. The ungrounded pots would not have to be set to the same value, in which case unbalanced limiting would occur. Many different types of limiter circuits can be devised, depending upon the required accuracy. The ideal diode limiter discussed in Example 8.2 suffers from an inaccuracy called "softness." This means the output does not remain exactly limited to the same value as the input increases, but, rather, it also increases slightly beyond its initial limiting value. This is again due to the contact potential in any real diode and is overcome by using precision circuits that compensate for this characteristic. Some common "hard" limiter circuits are shown in Appendix B.

*example 8.3*

As a final example of the use of ideal diodes to generate some arbitrary transfer characteristic, consider an operational amplifier connected in the configura-

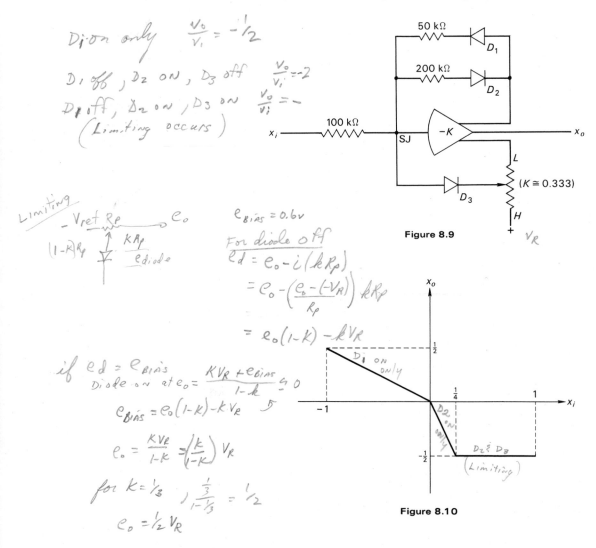

Figure 8.9

Figure 8.10

tion as shown in Figure 8.9. Using relation (8.4), it can be seen that limiting takes place for all values of positive input signals that cause the output to exceed $-0.500$. For all negative inputs, diodes $D_2$ and $D_3$ have no effect because they are always reverse-biased. Diode $D_1$, however, is switched "on" and a gain $-\frac{1}{2}$ device results. The reader can confirm that the diode circuit of Figure 8.9 has a transfer characteristic as shown in Figure 8.10.

The three examples above should provide the reader with techniques for analyzing any diode circuit or, as is more commonly the problem, they should suggest methods of constructing diode circuits required to mechanize some arbitrary nonlinear system. As has been noted, precision diode circuits that generate some common nonlinear systems are listed in Appendix B.

As first mentioned in Section 8.0, magnitude scaling of transfer characteristics is normally required. In all the above examples the range of input and output variables was assumed never to exceed plus or minus unity. This means that both input and output variables were automatically normalized to unity; but since this is not always the case, we need to make use of the normalized variable notation as defined in Section 4.1.

To understand the scaling of transfer characteristics, consider the following example.

**8.3
transfer
characteristic
normalization**

### example 8.4

Suppose that, in the analysis of a nonlinear mechanical system, the following equation results:

$$M\ddot{y} + B\dot{y} + F(y) = Au_{-1}(t) \tag{8.5}$$

$F(y)$ is a nonlinear spring force term that can be represented by a transfer characteristic as shown in Figure 8.11. This transfer characteristic could be obtained using the type of dual-side limiter described in Example 8.2. However, since the limiter output $F(y)$ can not exceed the range minus one to plus one, some type of magnitude scaling is clearly required. Further, the input $y$ would come from another amplifier in the circuit and thus it, too, would have to be magnitude scaled. In this example, suppose that, based on some knowledge of the system, we know that the displacement $y$ never exceeds 8 m. Thus we could choose

$$y_N = 10 \text{ m} \tag{8.6}$$

so that

$$x_y = \frac{y}{y_N} = \frac{y}{10} \tag{8.7}$$

This enables us to normalize the horizontal axis of the transfer characteristic.

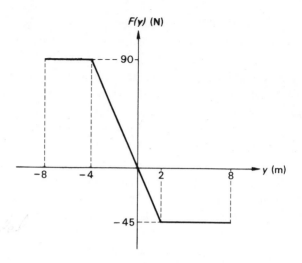

**Figure 8.11**

The scaling of the output $F(y)$ is done in exactly the same manner. Since the maximum force is 90 N, we could choose some $F_N$ to be

$$F_N = 100 \text{ N} \tag{8.8}$$

Then, in a manner analogous to (8.7), we have

$$x_F(x) = \frac{F(y)}{F_N} = \frac{F(y)}{100} \tag{8.9}$$

Using (8.7) and (8.9), the scaled transfer characteristic shown in Figure 8.12 is obtained. The reader should note that there are no units associated with the normalized variables $x_y$ and $x_F(x)$. The normalized transfer characteristic can easily be generated using the precision limiter circuit shown in Section B.4.

The scaling of the basic equation of motion is carried out using the multiply-and-divide procedure illustrated in Example 4.2. To do this, estimates of the maximum values of $\ddot{y}$ and $\dot{y}$ would have to be made so that values for $\ddot{y}_N$ and $\dot{y}_N$ could be chosen. Having these, the equation could be scaled as follows:

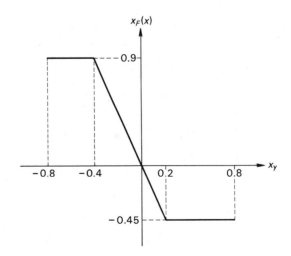

**Figure 8.12**

$$M\ddot{y}_N \left(\frac{\ddot{y}}{\ddot{y}_N}\right) + B\dot{y}_N \left(\frac{\dot{y}}{\dot{y}_N}\right) + F_N \left(\frac{F(y)}{F_N}\right) = Au_{-1}(t) \qquad (8.10)$$

which yields

$$\ddot{x}_y + \left(\frac{B\dot{y}_N}{M\ddot{y}_N}\right)\dot{x}_y + \left(\frac{F_N}{M\ddot{y}_N}\right) x_F(x) = \left(\frac{A}{M\ddot{y}_N}\right) u_{-1}(t) \qquad (8.11)$$

Thus, in this example, the nonlinear term has been easily handled by means of a normalized transfer characteristic.

**8.4 summary**

The introductory transfer characteristic concepts discussed in this chapter have been included to illustrate some basic nonlinear techniques frequently encountered in systems analysis. The ideal diode circuits shown are to be considered only in terms of their value in illustrating the basic concepts; for any real problem the precision circuits shown in Appendix B should be used. Many other diode circuits may be found in the literature.

As a final comment, it should be noted that the strip-chart recorder discussed in Appendix A can not be used to plot the type of transfer characteristic defined in this chapter. Instead, an $X$-$Y$ recorder must be used. This is a very common type of analog computer output device. It differs from the strip-chart recorder in that an arbitrary signal may be applied to both the $X$ (longitudinal) and $Y$ (transverse) axes. The time base generator discussed in Example 3.4 can be used with an $X$-$Y$ recorder to obtain time recordings if desired.

## PROBLEMS

8.1. A typical silicon rectifier diode has a reverse, or back, resistance $R_r$ of 1 M$\Omega$ and a forward resistance $R_f$ of 10 $\Omega$.

    (a) Construct an appropriate complete circuit model for the actual diode.
    (b) If the actual diode is assumed to be ideal, what would be its circuit model under conditions of forward-bias? Under conditions of reverse-bias?

8.2. Consider an operational amplifier wired as shown in Figure 8.13. Assuming an ideal diode, sketch the transfer characteristic for this device.

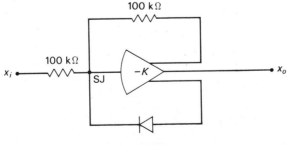

**Figure 8.13**

8.3. The operational amplifier configuration of Example 8.2 uses an ungrounded pot connected to an amplifier output. Assuming the wiper arm of the pot is located at some position $A$ (with corresponding output $x_A$), then the equivalent circuit of the pot is as shown in Figure 8.14. $K$ is the pot setting and $R_p$ represents the total end-to-end pot resistance. Recognizing that $x_A$ is zero when $x_o$ is exactly equal to the limited output $x_L$ derive relation (8.4).

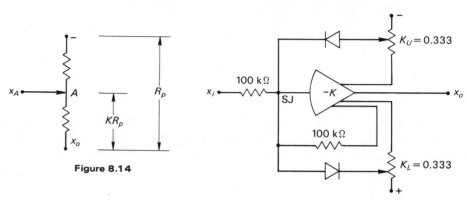

Figure 8.14

Figure 8.15

8.4. Consider an operational amplifier wired as shown in Figure 8.15. Assuming both diodes are ideal, sketch the transfer characteristic.

8.5. The circuit for a precision fullwave rectifier is shown in Figure B.3, Section B.2. The schematic shows three inputs being summed at the second amplifier to give the desired output as shown in Figure B.4. Sketch these input transfer characteristics and show that their inverted sum is as shown in Figure B.4. (*Hint:* Refer to Figures B.1 and B.2.)

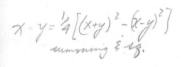

8.6. The quarter-square multiplier is a very common and very useful, analog computing element. This device was not discussed in Chapter 2, where only linear components were described. The quarter-square multiplier derives its name from the identity

$$4xy = (x + y)^2 - (x - y)^2$$

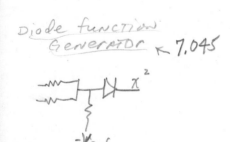

Here the product $xy$ can be obtained by summation and squaring. In the generalized (not actual) flow diagram shown in Figure 8.16, label the output of each element and show that the product $xy$ is obtained at the P1 output. All the gains are unity, except for the gain 2 on A2, as noted.

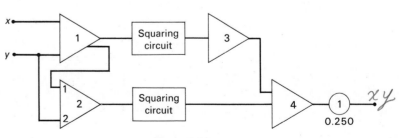

Figure 8.16

8.7. Assume that the two properly scaled normalized variables $x_u$ and $x_v$ are being multiplied by a quarter-square multiplier. What is an expression for the normalizing constant associated with the normalized output $x_w = -x_u x_v$? Is there a danger that the amplifier at whose output this product appears will overload?

8.8. Quarter-square multipliers require both plus and minus inputs of both multiplicands. One flow diagram symbol is as shown in Figure 8.17. Using two such

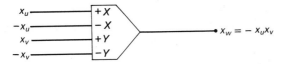

**Figure 8.17**

multipliers, develop a flow diagram to solve the general second-order equation

$$\ddot{x} + 2\zeta\omega_n\dot{x} + \omega_n^2 x = Au_{-1}(t)$$

such that the damping ratio $\zeta$ and the natural frequency $\omega_n$ can be set independently. Assume that no scaling is necessary. (Recall that the use of the symbol $x$ for the dependent variable indicates it is a normalized variable.) The initial conditions are all zero.

8.9. Sketch the transfer characteristic of each of the circuits shown in Figure 8.18. Assume that all diodes are ideal.

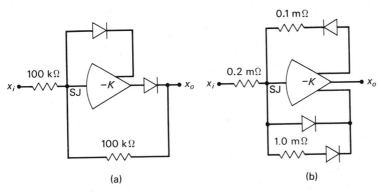

**Figure 8.18**

8.10. Given the nonlinear differential equation

$$\dot{y} + 100y|y| = 0$$

with

$$y(0) = 18 \text{ m}$$

Choose normalizing constants and a time scale factor, magnitude scale, and construct a flow diagram to solve this system.

# chapter nine

**9.0**
**introduction**
The theory and application of the analog computer for use in the simulation of arbitrary system transfer functions is very comprehensive and involved and could easily be the subject of an entire volume. The purpose of this chapter is to introduce the concept of a transfer function and to show one procedure for simulating such functions on the computer. The adjective "one" must be emphasized; several techniques exist, each having certain advantages and disadvantages. The ability to handle transfer functions on the computer provides the engineer with a very powerful tool of synthesis and analysis. Very complicated systems can often be analyzed in terms of more easily-handled "pieces" of the total system, and the total system response can then be obtained by considering the responses of the several parts. Conversely, systems, or components thereof, can often be synthesized by measuring the response of a computer-simulated model of the system. In the latter case, the system transfer function could be simulated on the computer, the input forcing function could be applied, and the parameters of the system model could be varied in order to achieve certain response specifications.

The entire concept of transfer functions presumes the presence of a *linear* system. A transfer function cannot be defined, at least in the usual sense, for a nonlinear system. Further, as will be seen in the next section, the establish-

# transfer function simulation

ment of a system transfer function is based on the assumption that all initial conditions in the system are zero.

Before considering the use of the analog computer for simulation of transfer functions, we should first review their theory and definition. This is done in the next section. A knowledge of basic Laplace transform techniques on the part of the reader is assumed (any text on linear system theory can be consulted for review if desired).

To define a system transfer function, consider the equation of motion for a second-order linear system

**9.1 transfer functions**

$$a\ddot{y} + b\dot{y} + cy = kf(t) \qquad (9.1)$$

We assume a second-order system here only for simplicity; higher-order systems are handled in exactly the same manner. As a matter of fact, the real usefulness of transfer function analysis is exhibited more clearly when higher-order systems are encountered. Relation (9.1) may be rearranged as

$$\ddot{y} + \left(\frac{b}{a}\right)\dot{y} + \left(\frac{c}{a}\right)y = \left(\frac{k}{a}\right)f(t) \qquad (9.2)$$

Note that $f(t)$, the forcing function, has not been specified. Assuming all initial conditions are zero (an assumption implicit in the definition of a transfer function), we can Laplace transform (9.2) and obtain

$$\left[ s^2 + \left(\frac{b}{a}\right) s + \left(\frac{c}{a}\right) \right] Y(s) = \left(\frac{k}{a}\right) F(s) \tag{9.3}$$

Now, the transfer function $G(s)$ is defined to be the ratio of the Laplace transformed output $Y(s)$ to the Laplace transformed input $F(s)$,

$$G(s) = \frac{Y(s)}{F(s)} = \frac{k/a}{s^2 + (b/a)s + (c/a)} \tag{9.4}$$

Since we have

$$Y(s) = G(s)F(s) \tag{9.5}$$

we may think of the transfer function in block diagram notation, as shown in Figure 9.1. Since the transfer function is defined to be the output over the

Figure 9.1 *Block diagram notation*

input (in the $s$ domain), we see that it is independent of the forcing function. $G(s)$ is a function only of the system; it is valid for any input we may require.

### example 9.1

As a simple example of the derivation of a transfer function, consider the mechanical system shown in Example 3.1. From Equation (3.2) we have

$$\ddot{x} + \left(\frac{B}{M}\right) \dot{x} + \left(\frac{K}{M}\right) x = \left(\frac{1}{M}\right) f(t) \tag{9.6}$$

This is Laplace transformed to yield

$$\left[ s^2 + \left(\frac{B}{M}\right) s + \left(\frac{K}{M}\right) \right] X(s) = \left(\frac{1}{M}\right) F(s) \tag{9.7}$$

Or, using the values given in the example,

$$[s^2 + 0.160s + 0.640]X(s) = 0.500F(s) \tag{9.8}$$

Thus, the transfer function is

$$G(s) = \frac{X(s)}{F(s)} = \frac{0.500}{s^2 + 0.160s + 0.640} \tag{9.9}$$

A transfer function can be defined in terms of any output and any input. For example, in a series $RLC$ circuit, the output could be taken as a voltage across an element, as the loop current, as the charge, etc. In a given system we may wish to define several transfer functions in order to find certain responses to a given forcing function. The over-all transfer function of a system may sometimes be thought of as the product of the transfer functions of the individual parts. For instance, consider the block diagram in Figure 9.2. Using the definition of a transfer function, the reader should confirm that Figure 9.2 can be

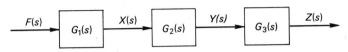

**Figure 9.2**  *Cascaded block diagram*

represented as shown in Figure 9.3. The over-all transfer function $G(s)$ is given by

$$G(s) = G_1(s)G_2(s)G_3(s) \tag{9.10}$$

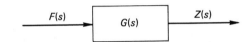

**Figure 9.3**  *Resultant block diagram*

The brief discussion of transfer functions given above illustrates their value in linear systems analysis. We now consider the simulation of several simple transfer functions with the help of examples.

There are several methods we can employ to mechanize transfer functions on the analog computer. One obvious method involves a reformulation of the differential equation from which the transfer function was originally obtained. This is done by "cross-multiplying" the defined relation, much as (9.4) could be cross-multiplied to yield the original equation given in (9.2).This technique, while straightforward, can introduce serious problems for some types of transfer functions and/or forcing functions. Another standard approach, which we introduce here, involves a modification of the cross-multiplying technique such that the individual parts of the transfer function are programmed separately. The technique is illustrated by several examples.

**9.2 computer simulation**

While the concept of transfer function simulation may seem simple and straightforward, the application of the technique, especially with regards to scaling, is not so easy. The difficulty involved in scaling can be pointed out if one recalls that in a transfer function the input is unspecified and all initial conditions are zero! Thus, the simple techniques for estimation of maximum values, given in Chapter 7, are not applicable. Therefore, the scaling of the transfer function must be made an integral part of the programming procedure.

*example 9.2*

For a simple first example, consider the transfer function

$$G(s) = \frac{Y(s)}{F(s)} = \frac{1}{(s+4)(s+2)} \tag{9.11}$$

We wish to simulate this transfer function on the analog computer such that for some given input forcing function $f(t)$ the output $y(t)$ could be obtained at the output of an integrating or summing amplifier. To do this it is convenient to utilize the concept of cascading suggested by (9.10) and write

$$G(s) = \frac{Y(s)}{F(s)} = \frac{Z(s)}{F(s)} \cdot \frac{Y(s)}{Z(s)} = \left(-\frac{1}{s+4}\right)\left(-\frac{1}{s+2}\right) \tag{9.12}$$

Thus, we program

$$\frac{Z(s)}{F(s)} = -\frac{1}{s+4} \tag{9.13}$$

and follow this, in series, with a program for

$$\frac{Y(s)}{Z(s)} = -\frac{1}{s+2} \tag{9.14}$$

The variable $Z(s)$ is certainly not defined by (9.11) but is simply a "dummy variable" to emphasize the split of $G(s)$ into two factors. The minus signs are conveniently included to take account of the inherent sign change in the amplifiers used to mechanize the two functions.

If (9.13) is considered separately for the time being, we may cross-multiply to obtain

$$sZ(s) + 4Z(s) = -F(s) \tag{9.15}$$

This equation can be solved for the negative of the highest power of $s$ that multiplies the variable $Z(s)$:

$$-sZ(s) = 4Z(s) + F(s) \tag{9.16}$$

This is in a form amenable to the indirect programming procedure introduced in Section 3.1. We may sum at the input of integrators when handling transfer functions because the objections to this practice, mentioned in Section 3.1, are not applicable here. It should be clear that the flow diagram shown in Figure 9.4 correctly mechanizes Equation (9.16). Figure 9.4 is an unscaled

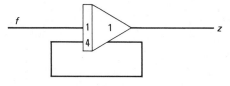

**Figure 9.4**

partial program for $G(s)$. The scaling will be considered later, after the complete transfer function is obtained.

The second "piece" of $G(s)$, given by (9.14), results in a relation analogous to (9.16); namely,

$$-sY(s) = 2Y(s) + Z(s) \tag{9.17}$$

The program for this is shown in Figure 9.5.

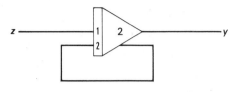

**Figure 9.5**

If the two partial flow diagrams are now connected in series (that is, "cascaded" as illustrated in Figure 9.2), we have the configuration shown in Figure 9.6. This program represents an *unscaled* simulation of the total system transfer function given by Equation (9.11). As such, it is unsatisfactory for actual operation.

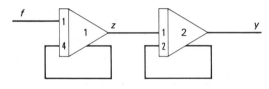

**Figure 9.6**

To correct for magnitude scaling, the double-and-halve rule (introduced in Section 4.2) is employed in a systematic fashion. As previously emphasized, the steps taken to accomplish scaling should be carefully recorded on the Analog Computer Worksheet. If the integrator gains are equalized, we have the flow diagram shown in Figure 9.7. In this simple example, the application of the double-and-halve rule was accomplished in one step. This is not generally true.

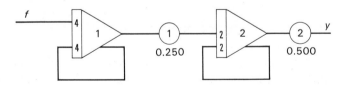

**Figure 9.7**

As mentioned in Section 6.1, we always time scale an analog computer problem so that no integrator gain exceeds unity. In the above simulation, we would then probably choose $n \geq 4$. If, for convenience of illustration, we choose $n = 4$, we divide each integrator gain setting by 4. This results in a program as shown in Figure 9.8. We might be inclined to consider this program as a final result for the simulation of $G(s)$, but closer examination indicates that, as a result of the time scaling operations, we need to magnitude

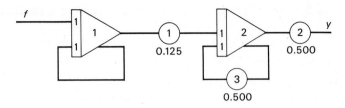

**Figure 9.8**

rescale. To see this, consider applying a positive unit step input to A1. In other words, assume that

$$f(t) = +1.0u_{-1}(t) \tag{9.18}$$

A1 integrates until its output reaches minus unity, at which time the output of P1 (input to A2) equals $-0.125$. The output of A2 tends to go positive under the influence of this small negative input. However, because of the feedback path containing P3, we see that, when the A2 output reaches $+0.250$, the net input to A2 is zero. Thus, the output of A2 never exceeds 0.250 and we would be operating the amplifier over essentially only 25% of its design range.

The obvious solution to the above scaling problem is to multiply the A2 input (pot 1) by a factor of 4 and to reduce its output (pot 2) by the same factor. Of course, this procedure does not change the setting of P3. The resulting program is shown in Figure 9.9. Now, the output of A2 reaches a full $+1.00$

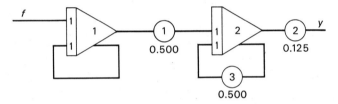

**Figure 9.9**

before the net input to A2 reaches zero and integration ceases. Thus, assuming a unit step input, both integrators operate over their full dynamic range. Since, on a normalized basis, the magnitude of the input can never exceed unity, we have achieved good magnitude and time scaling. The flow diagram given in Figure 9.9 represents a good simulation of $G(s)$ given by Equation (9.11).

Example 9.2 above was developed in detail to illustrate the general procedure to be followed when simulating a transfer function. A summary of this procedure will be given in Section 9.3. Before doing this, however, it may be useful to consider other examples.

**example 9.3**

The previous example illustrated the simulation of a transfer function whose characteristic equation (the denominator polynomial in $s$) was represented by two first-order factors. Many times, however, one needs to simulate a transfer function which represents an underdamped second-order system. For these cases, the damping ratio $\zeta$ lies between zero and unity, and the characteristic equation cannot be factored into two real roots. For such cases, and for higher-order systems, it is necessary to simulate the transfer function directly. To illustrate this point, consider the transfer function

$$G(s) = \frac{Y(s)}{F(s)} = -\frac{4}{s^2 + 2s + 4} \tag{9.19}$$

Here, as before, the minus sign is included in recognition of the inherent amplifier sign changes. Its deletion would simply result in the requirement for one additional amplifier in the mechanization process.

Equation (9.19) can be cross-multiplied and solved for the negative of the highest power of $s$ that multiplies the output to yield

$$-s^2 Y(s) = 4F(s) + 2s Y(s) + 4Y(s) \tag{9.20}$$

From this, we can form the *unscaled* flow diagram shown in Figure 9.10. This is an unsatisfactory simulation and must be magnitude and time scaled.

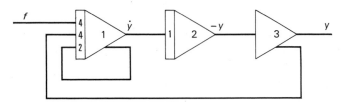

**Figure 9.10**

As a first step, the integrator gains are equalized by multiplying all inputs to A1 by 0.500 and by dividing the output by the same amount. Dividing the output by 0.500 places a gain 2 on the A2 input (Figure 9.11). With all inte-

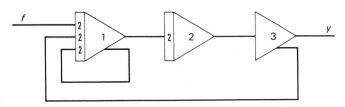

**Figure 9.11**

grator gains now equal to 2 we can, for convenience, choose a time scale factor

$$n = 2 \tag{9.21}$$

Normally, a slightly larger value for $n$ would be chosen, because integrator gains should be reduced to about 0.500. The resulting flow diagram is shown in Figure 9.12.

At this point, we might be inclined to say that a workable simulation had been achieved. Although no really serious problems arise if we run this simulation, A2 and A3 do overrange (the maximum magnitude of their output

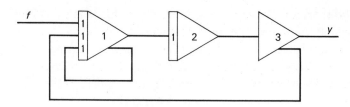

Figure 9.12

reaches about 1.17 for a unit step function input). Hence, magnitude rescaling is required. This requirement is quite obvious if one notes from (9.19) that

$$\zeta = 0.5 \qquad \text{and} \qquad y_{\text{final}}(t) = -1.00 \tag{9.22}$$

Thus, while the steady state response to a unit step function input causes no overloading, the transient overshoot in the response causes an approximate 17% overrange. This is again corrected by halving-and-doubling around A2 and A3. Doubling the A3 output places a corresponding gain 2 on the middle input to A1. The resulting output of A3 is then $0.500y$. The final flow diagram for this simulation is shown in Figure 9.13. The reader can wire this program

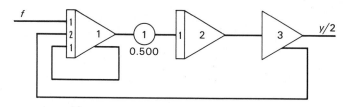

Figure 9.13

and confirm that good scaling has been achieved. The approximate maximum amplifier outputs are (for a positive unit step input)

$$
\begin{aligned}
\text{A1} &= -0.550 \\
\text{A2} &= +0.585 \\
\text{A3} &= -0.585
\end{aligned}
\tag{9.23}
$$

Neither of the two previous examples is of the type having powers of $s$ in the numerator. Transfer functions having both zeros and poles present slightly more difficult problems. As a final example in this section, we consider such a transfer function.

### example 9.4

Given the following transfer function having poles at $-0.100 \pm j0.995$ and a zero at $-1.00$:

$$G(s) = \frac{Y(s)}{F(s)} = \frac{s + 1}{s^2 + 0.2s + 1} \tag{9.24}$$

We note that $\zeta = 0.1$ and $\omega_n = 1.00$ rad/sec. Following the other examples, we may solve for the negative of the highest-order output term and obtain

$$-s^2 Y(s) = Y(s) - F(s) + 0.2s\, Y(s) - sF(s) \tag{9.25}$$

To program this directly would require having available the first derivative of the input. Since differentiation is usually not performed on an analog computer, we divide (9.25) through by $s$ and obtain

$$-s Y(s) = \left(-\frac{1}{s}\right)[F(s) - Y(s)] + [0.2\,Y(s) - F(s)] \tag{9.26}$$

Note that the quantity $-1/s$ has been factored out of the first term on the right-hand side of (9.26). Since division by $s$ in the frequency domain corresponds to integration in the time domain, the first term implies an integration of the quantity $F(s) - Y(s)$. The reader should confirm that the unscaled flow diagram shown in Figure 9.14 is a correct mechanization of (9.26).

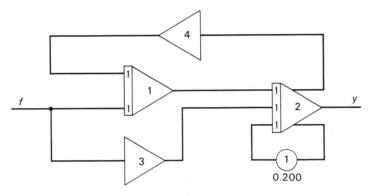

**Figure 9.14**

In this example, $\omega_n$ is exactly 1.00 rad/sec so, if integrator gains of 1 can be tolerated, no time scaling is required. However, for a unit step input, the final value of the response $y(t)$ is 1.00. Since $\zeta$ is 0.100, the overshoot in the underdamped response is about 70%. Thus, serious overloading occurs. With no rescaling, the maximum value of the A1 output is about +1.70 and that of A2 is about +2.05. This overloading could essentially be corrected by halving-and-doubling, but a "safer" amount to reduce the levels by is a factor of three. If this is done, the final flow diagram results as shown in Figure 9.15. The

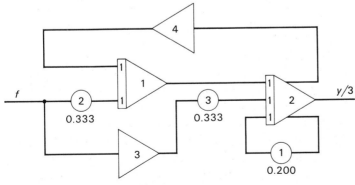

**Figure 9.15**

reader can confirm that, with a positive unit step input, the maximum output of A1 is about $+0.570$ and the maximum output of A2 is about $+0.680$.

In the above examples, summing was done at an integrator input. As mentioned earlier, the objections to this practice, discussed in Section 3.1, are generally not applicable in transfer function simulation. However, unless we have many transfer functions to simulate and have a limited number of amplifiers, it is still a good practice to sum at the input to a summer. Slightly better accuracy may accrue and the rescaling operations are simplified. Also, quantities such as the time constant $\tau$ in a first-order system, the damping ratio $\zeta$ and the frequency $\omega_n$ in a second-order system, and the time scale factor $n$ are more easily recognized.

**9.3
summary**

The above examples have illustrated the simulation of some simple transfer functions on the analog computer. Many different techniques exist for the handling of transfer functions, and most advanced analog computer textbooks contain extensive material on this topic. The purpose of this chapter was simply to introduce the theory so that the interested reader can, by further reading and making analogies, develop the flow diagrams for those specific transfer functions he may encounter.

The procedures discussed and followed in the examples may be summarized by considering the series of steps outlined as follows:

(1) Arrange the transfer function $G(s)$ in factored form (if factorable) such that the numerator and denominator polynomials in each factor have a coefficient of unity for the highest power of $s$. Then, simulate each factor separately (in accordance with the following steps) and cascade the simulations.

(2) Cross-multiply the transfer function; that is, take the numerator of $G(s)$ times the input $F(s)$, and the denominator times the output $Y(s)$.

(3) Divide both sides of the resulting equation by the highest power of $s$ that appears as a coefficient of the input $F(s)$. (This eliminates the necessity of requiring derivatives of the input.)

(4) Solve for the negative of the term having the output $Y(s)$ multiplied by the highest power of $s$.

(5) Group all terms on the right-hand side of the resulting equation that are now divided by successive powers of $s$. Factor the quantity $-1/s$ from these terms as often as possible. Repeat this procedure until $s$ no longer appears in any denominator.

(6) Program the above unnormalized equation. Since the negative of the highest-order output term appears on the left-hand side (from step 4), and since all terms multiplied by $-1/s$, $-1/s^2$, etc. are grouped on the right-hand side (from step 5), programming is essentially a

simple application of the indirect technique discussed in Chapter 3. Summing may be done on integrators if desired, or if insufficient numbers of amplifiers are available to allow the use of summers.

(7) Equalize integrator gains (at least insofar as is possible) by using the double-and-halve rule (discussed in Section 4.2). Keep a careful record of the adjustments that are made.

(8) Time scale the resulting program by choosing a time scale factor $n$, such that all integrator gains are reduced to a maximum of 1.00. Reduce the gains to about 0.500 if possible; this allows for the use of nearly any type of plotting equipment.

(9) Check the scaling of the simulation by running it with a reduced step function input. For example, use $f(t) = 0.1u_{-1}(t)$. Then, if no amplifier in the program has an absolute maximum over 0.1, the simulation can run for inputs of 10 times this value. If any amplifier has an output that indicates that overloading would occur, magnitude rescale using the double-and-halve rule. As a final check, run the simulation with a full step function input and check every amplifier for overloading (or, conversely, for outputs so small as to degrade the accuracy).

The systematic application of the procedure summarized in the above nine steps should result in a workable simulation of most transfer functions commonly encountered in linear system analysis. The reader should note the manner in which each of the given applicable steps was followed in the examples of the previous section.

Finally, it should be pointed out that no provision was made in the scaling of transfer functions to account for the phenomenon of resonance that occurs in lightly-damped systems when sinusoidal inputs are applied. For sinusoidal forcing functions whose magnitude is approximately unity and whose frequency is near $\omega_n$ of the system, serious overloading could occur. However, this situation can be easily corrected using the double-and-halve rule. Preliminary scaling guidance can be obtained by using normalized response curves for second-order systems, which can be found in nearly any text on linear system theory (for example, see reference 5).

## PROBLEMS

9.1. Given the *RLC* series electrical network of Problem 6.1, with element values as listed. Find the numerical value of the transfer function

$$G(s) = \frac{V_C(s)}{E(s)}$$

9.2. Figure 9.16 is an idealized single-degree-of-freedom mechanical model for one wheel of an automobile suspension system. *M* represents mass, and *K* and *B* are translational spring stiffness and damping, respectively. The applied forcing

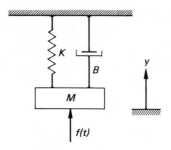

**Figure 9.16**

function is due to the road surface, but is unspecified. Find the transfer function

$$G(s) = \frac{Y(s)}{F(s)}$$

9.3. The system shown in Figure 9.17 represents an audio amplifier and speaker. The input voltage $v_i$ is fed through an *RC* filter and amplifier to a speaker, which is represented by the *RL* model. The output voltage $v_o$ is taken across the 10 Ω resistor as shown in Figure 9.17. Find the transfer functions $G_1(s)$ and $G_3(s)$, and the over-all system transfer function.

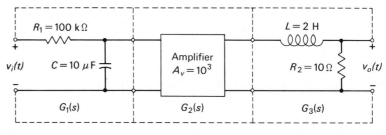

**Figure 9.17**

9.4. Figure 9.18 is an idealized two-degree-of-freedom mechanical model for the load on a servomotor, where

$$J = \text{moment of inertia}$$
$$B = \text{rotational damping constant}$$

$K$ = spring stiffness (reciprocal of compliance)
$T_a(t)$ = applied step function torque

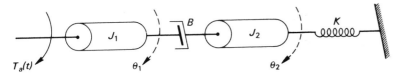

**Figure 9.18**

Write the two equations of motion of this system, in terms of $\theta_1$ and $\theta_2$, and then combine them to form the transfer function

$$G(s) = \frac{\theta_2(s)}{T_a(s)}$$

9.5.  The characteristic equation (denominator of the transfer function) of a second-order system may be arranged in the standard form

$$s^2 + 2\zeta\omega_n s + \omega_n^2$$

Sketch the poles of the transfer function (roots of the characteristic equation) as the damping ratio $\zeta$ varies from zero to values greater than unity. Can you identify the undamped natural frequency of oscillation $\omega_n$, the damped frequency $\omega_d$, and the damping ratio on the sketch?

9.6.  In Problem 9.5, the regions $\zeta = 0$, $0 < \zeta < 1$, $\zeta = 1$, and $\zeta > 1$ result in different responses of the second-order system to a step input. If the transfer function is of the form

$$G(s) = \frac{X(s)}{F(s)}$$

$$= \frac{1}{s^2 + 2\zeta\omega_n s + \omega_n^2}$$

where

$$F(s) = \frac{A}{s}$$

sketch the four types of responses. Show the final value (if applicable) in each case.

9.7.  Given the transfer function

$$G(s) = \frac{1}{s^2 + 15s + 50}$$

Develop an analog computer simulation for $G(s)$. Pay careful attention to magnitude and time scaling, and check to see if magnitude rescaling may be necessary.

9.8. Lead, or differentiating, circuits are frequently required in the compensation of feedback control systems.

(a) Show that the $RC$ circuit in Figure 9.19 has a transfer function of the form

$$\frac{s}{s+a}$$

(b) Show that, in the circuit (Figure 9.19), the output $v_2(t)$ is essentially equal to the derivative of the input $v_1(t)$ if the voltage across the resistor is small compared to the voltage across the capacitor.

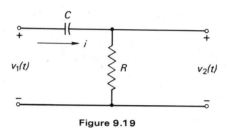

Figure 9.19

(c) Show that Figure 9.20 is an analog computer simulation of the same type of transfer function as given in part (a); that is, $s/(s+a)$.

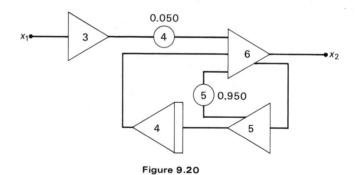

Figure 9.20

(d) What is an expression for the constant $a$ in the transfer function(a) in terms of the circuit elements shown in part (b)? What is its numerical value in the simulation of part (c)? How is this constant related to the first-order time constant $\tau$?

9.9. Consider the transfer function

$$G(s) = \frac{Z(s)}{F(s)}$$

$$= \frac{s+8}{(s+4)(s+2)}$$

Use the results of Problem 9.8 to develop an analog computer simulation of the system described by this transfer function.

(*Hint:* Write $G(s)$ as

$$G(s) = \frac{Y(s)}{F(s)} \cdot \frac{Z(s)}{Y(s)}$$

$$= \frac{1}{(s+4)(s+2)} \cdot \frac{(s+8)}{1}$$

Note that $Y(s)/F(s)$ is the same function as given in Example 9.2. Program $Z(s)/Y(s)$ by using the differentiator shown in Problem 9.8(c). A gain of 20 must be included at the differentiator output to account for the attenuation of that device.)

**9.10.** Given the transfer function

$$G(s) = \frac{s^2 + 0.2s + 1}{2s^3 + 6s^2 + 54s + 50}$$

Use the steps listed in Section 9.3 to program this function. A time scale factor of about 10 is required.

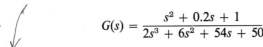

① Factor highest $S$ to that coeff. of has coeff. of 1

$$G = \frac{Y}{F} = \frac{1}{2} \frac{s^2 + 0.2s + 1}{s^3 + 3s^2 + 27s + 25}$$

② cross multi to obtain $Y = GZ$

$$s^3 Y + 3s^2 Y + 27s + 25Y = s^2 Z + 0.25 Z + Z$$

③ Divide by highest $S$ on input side

$$sY + 3Y + \frac{27}{s}Y + \frac{25}{s^2}Y = Z + \frac{0.2}{s}Z + \frac{Z}{s^2}$$

④ Solve for neg. of highest power of $s$ on $Y$

$$-sY = 3Y + \frac{27}{s}Y + \frac{25}{s^2}Y - Z - \frac{0.2}{s}Z - \frac{Z}{s^2}$$

⑤ Factor $\frac{1}{s}$ terms form RHS.

$$-sY = \left(-\frac{1}{s}\right)\left(-\frac{1}{s}\right)(25Y - Z) + \left(-\frac{1}{s}\right)(0.2Z - 27Y) + (3Y - Z)$$

⑥ Program using successive integration

integration in time domain

$= \frac{1}{s}$ in $S$ domain

$-\int dt = -\frac{1}{s}$

$\frac{z}{F} = \frac{1}{2} \rightarrow Z = \frac{F}{2}$

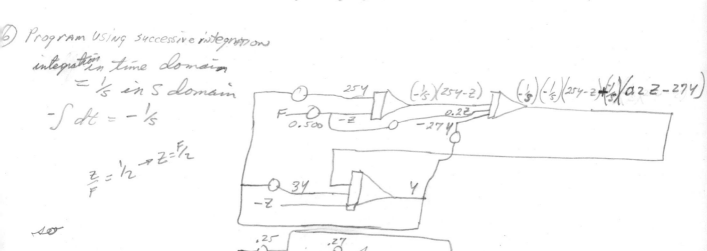

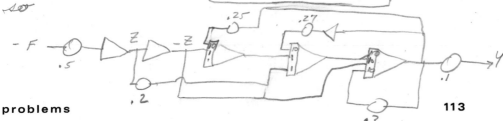

# chapter ten

**10.0**
**introduction**
The previous chapters of this text have been concerned with topics related to the solution of differential equations. Indeed, the development of analog computation grew out of the need for a quick and convenient method for solving such equations. The solution of algebraic equations, on the other hand, is usually accomplished using a digital computer. This does not mean that either machine cannot be used to solve both types of equations. Common algorithms, such as the Runge-Kutta or Milne predictor-corrector, are available for digital solutions of differential equations. The analog computer is usually faster, however; for example, an extremely nonlinear differential equation can often be solved on a modern repetitive-operation analog computer in several hundred milliseconds or less. The solution of the same equation on a fast digital computer could take several seconds of iteration time.

The solution of high-order algebraic equations is usually done on a digital computer, by programming the machine to use one of several approximation methods (bisection, Newton-Raphson, etc.). However, the real roots of such equations can also be found using the analog computer. In this chapter, we discuss one technique for finding the real roots of a polynomial on an analog computer. The method we use is an adaptation of a technique due to Forrest (reference 6). It uses only those linear computing elements covered in Chapter 2. The general technique is explained in the next section and then a compre-

# algebraic equations

hensive example, illustrating the details, is given. For comparison, the same problem is then solved using the digital computer. Such a problem illustrates that the analog computer is not, as some authors have implied, merely a "glorified slide rule."[1]

**10.1 determination of polynomial roots**

Suppose one seeks to obtain the real roots of a polynomial equation given in the general form

$$z = A_1 y^{b_1} + A_2 y^{b_2} + \cdots + A_n y^{b_n} \tag{10.1}$$

That is, we wish to solve for the values of $y$ for which $z$ equals zero. The general equation might be graphed as shown in Figure 10.1.

The technique to be used here to solve the general polynomial equation involves a substitution that converts the variables $y$ and $z$ into functions of time. Specifically, we use

$$y = y_N e^{-t} \tag{10.2}$$

If this substitution is made term-by-term in (10.1), we represent the result by

$$z = z_1 + z_2 + \cdots + z_n \tag{10.3}$$

[1] Kuo, S. S., *Numerical Methods and Computers* (Reading, Mass.: Addison-Wesley Publishing Co., Inc., 1965), page 3.

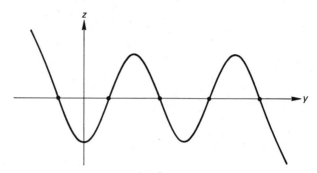

**Figure 10.1**  *Sketch of a fifth-order polynomial*

Each $z_i$ term is now a function of time, and can be programmed separately. The amplifier outputs representing each $z_i$ term are then summed to obtain $z$ as a function of $y$.

To see this, consider the first term in (10.1),

$$z_1 = A_1 y^{b_1} \tag{10.4}$$

Using (10.2), we obtain

$$z_1 = A_1(y_N e^{-t})^{b_1} = A_1 y_N^{b_1} e^{-b_1 t} \tag{10.5}$$

We can obtain a program for this function using the implicit programming technique discussed in Section 3.3. To do this, we differentiate (10.5) to obtain

$$\dot{z}_1 = -b_1 A_1 y_N^{b_1} e^{-b_1 t} = -b_1 z_1 \tag{10.6}$$

This equation must be scaled using the normalizing constants $\dot{z}_{1_N}$ and $z_{1_N}$,

$$\dot{z}_{1_N}\left(\frac{\dot{z}_1}{\dot{z}_{1_N}}\right) = -b_1 z_{1_N}\left(\frac{z_1}{z_{1_N}}\right) \tag{10.7}$$

Or, in terms of normalized variables,

$$\dot{x}_{z_1} = -b_1\left(\frac{z_{1_N}}{\dot{z}_{1_N}}\right) x_{z_1} \tag{10.8}$$

If we used indirect programming techniques on (10.8), we would require a pot in the $x_{z_1}$ feedback loop set to

$$b_1\left(\frac{z_{1_N}}{\dot{z}_{1_N}}\right) \tag{10.9}$$

However, the term enclosed by parentheses is exactly cancelled out by the integrator input pot setting. Since, in general, time scaling is also required, we have a net integrator gain of $b_1/n$. The only other quantity required in the programming of (10.8) is the value of the initial condition. This is given by

$$x_{z_1}(0) = \frac{z_1(0)}{z_N} = \frac{A_1 y_N^{b_1}}{z_N} \tag{10.10}$$

The resulting program for the $z_1$ term in (10.1) is then as shown in Figure 10.2.

We note from the above development that values for $y_N$ and $z_N$ must be estimated. An estimate for $\dot{z}_N$ is not required because it does not appear in the program. The value for $y_N$ should be chosen to be a "good" number and

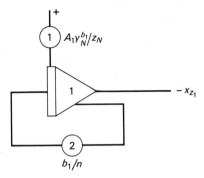

**Figure 10.2** *Partial flow diagram*

must be larger than the largest root. If only the roots over a restricted interval are desired, then $y_N$ must be chosen larger than the absolute value of the largest endpoint. A corresponding value for $z_N$ can be obtained by estimating the maximum magnitude for $z$ over the interval of interest. These restrictions are not severe because overly conservative estimates (too large) only compress the solution into a smaller range, thus reducing accuracy. Better estimates can always be obtained once the problem is initially run on the computer.

The partial flow diagram for the first term, shown in Figure 10.2, is repeated for all the remaining terms in Equation (10.1). A generalized program is as shown in Figure 10.3. Since this method requires (or results in) a plot of

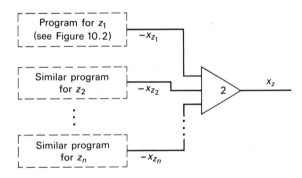

**Figure 10.3** *Complete flow diagram*

$z$ versus $y$, an $X$-$Y$ recorder is required. The variable $y$, which is plotted on the $X$ axis, is obtained from (10.2) and uses a program as shown in Figure 10.4.

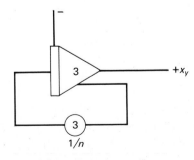

**Figure 10.4** *Flow diagram for variable y*

This term can actually be obtained from the program for $z_{n-1}$, as the following example points out.

The above discussion presumed the presence of real *positive* roots of (10.1). If negative roots are sought, the substitution

$$y = -y_N e^{-t} \tag{10.11}$$

is used in place of (10.2). This does not affect our development, except that the sign of the initial condition reference changes on those integrators whose output represents the *odd power* terms of (10.1). The IC reference also changes on the program for $x_y$, but the sign of the IC reference does not change on those integrators representing the *even power* terms in (10.1).

The technique just outlined in general terms is now illustrated by means of a simple example.

### example 10.1

Consider a cubic equation in $y$ given by

$$z = y^3 - 12.6y^2 + 49.1y - 58.5 \tag{10.12}$$

Exact formulas, of course, exist for obtaining the roots of such a simple polynomial. However, high-order algebraic equations cannot, in general, be solved (factored) analytically, so computer solutions are required.

The range of the roots of a polynomial such as (10.12) can usually be easily determined. For this particular polynomial, we can determine that no sign changes, or inflection points, occur for $y > 8$. Hence, we can choose $y_N = 8$. Since $z(0)$ is equal to $-58.5$ and $z(8)$ is equal to $+39.9$, we can choose $z_N = 100$ as a conservative estimate. Then, following the manipulations of Equations (10.4) through (10.6), we have

$$z_1 = y^3 = y_N^3 e^{-3t} \tag{10.13}$$

and

$$\dot{z}_1 = -3z_1 \tag{10.14}$$

In this case, $b_1 = 3$. Since the integrator gain setting reduces to simply $b_1/n$, we can choose a time scale factor $n = 10$, because $b_1 = 3$ is the largest power in our equation.

Following (10.10), we obtain the initial condition

$$x_{z_1}(0) = \frac{y_N^3}{z_N} = \frac{512}{100} = 5.12 \tag{10.15}$$

This is accomplished by using a plus reference as an IC, with a pot set to 0.512 following the $x_{z_1}$ integrator and a gain 10 on the final summer. The pot in the feedback path is set to 0.300 due to our choice of time scale factor. The partial flow diagram (for the first term in (10.12)) is then as shown in Figure 10.5. The remaining three terms (one of which is simply the constant $z_4 = -58.5$) are handled in exactly the same manner as $z_1$ was. The program for $x_y$ is obtained as shown in Figure 10.4. The reader should confirm that the complete flow diagram for this example is as shown in Figure 10.6. As mentioned earlier, the normalized output $x_y$ could be taken using an inverter following A3. The plotter inputs shown yield the desired plot of $z$ versus $y$. The points at which $z = 0$ then represent roots of the polynomial. These values for $y$ can be read from the graph.

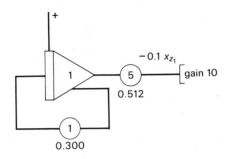

Figure 10.5

If an $X$-$Y$ recorder is not available, or if a plot of $z$ versus $y$ is not required, the roots can be read directly off the computer voltmeter. On the computer described in Appendix A, the null comparison method may be used. On computers having a digital voltmeter, the roots may also be read directly. To do this, one needs only to address A5 and, when that output is zero, to note the corresponding value of the output of A4. This is done by switching the computer to HOLD when A5 is zero. Since

$$y = x_y y_N \qquad (10.16)$$

the roots can easily be found.

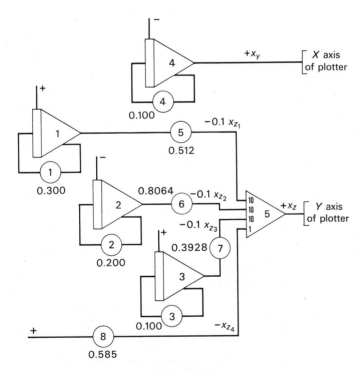

Figure 10.6

In this example, the following values should be read from the voltmeter as the output of A5 goes through zero

$$0.7744, \quad 0.4965, \quad 0.2887 \tag{10.17}$$

Using (10.16), with $y_N = 8$, we should have the following final factored result for a solution to (10.12):

$$z = (y - 6.1952)(y - 3.9720)(y - 2.3096) \tag{10.18}$$

These values are quite close, as a multiplication out would show. A plot of $z$ versus $y$ is shown in Figure 10.7. The choice of $y_N = 8$ resulted in a slightly awkward scale, but the reader should confirm that, from the plot, the following roots can be read

$$z = (y - 6.18)(y - 3.91)(y - 2.32) \tag{10.19}$$

These values represent an acceptable level of accuracy. If the results of a digital computer solution (shown in Example 10.2) are taken as a standard, then the largest error in the graphically determined roots is about 4.17%. The

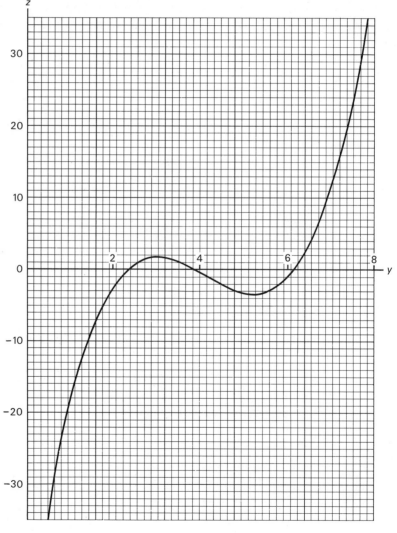

**Figure 10.7** *Graph of analog computer results; Plot of z versus y for Example 10.1*

largest error in the roots read from the voltmeter, as given in (10.18), is about 2.65%. A slightly more sophisticated program, using electronic comparators, should reduce the error to 1% or less.

The previous example has illustrated one method for using the analog computer to find the real roots of a polynomial equation. Other techniques exist and may be found in the literature.

### example 10.2

Although we have not discussed digital computation, it is interesting to simply present a digital computer solution of the polynomial equation given by (10.12) and solved in Example 10.1. We use the bisection approximation (reference 13). This procedure is slow, compared to some others, and requires an interval such that the value of the polynomial is different in sign at the end points. If these disadvantages can be overcome, the method is simple to apply

```
TIME: 2152  HOURS                          EXTENDED ALGOL COMPILATION


          BEGIN                                                    *
FORMAT       ID("CBCI09A                          BOX DFEE");*
FORMAT       HDN("THIS IS AN EXTENDED ALGOL PROGRAM FOR COMPUTING THE"*

             /"ROOTS OF A CUBIC EQUATION IN Y, USING THE BURROUGHS"/  *
             "B5500 COMPUTER.  THE ALGORITHM USED IS DERIVED FROM"/   *
             "THE BISECTION APPROXIMATION."/);

FILE         CARD"CBCI09A"(2,10), LINE 4(2,15);                    *
LABEL        EOF,L1,L2,L3,L4,L5;                                   *
REAL         L,R,Y,FY,FL;                                          *
INTEGER      COUNT;                                                *
ALPHA        N;                                                    *
$$ A TIMER                                                         *
             WRITE(LINE,ID); TIMER(0,LINE); WRITE(LINE,HDN);       *
             WRITE(LINE,<X31,"3",X8,"2">);                         *

             WRITE(LINE,<"THE POLYNOMIAL EQUATION IS:   Y  - 12.6Y  +"*
             " 49.1Y - 58.5 = 0"//>);                             *

L1:          READ(CARD,/,N,L,R)[EOF]; COUNT+0;                     *
             WRITE(LINE,<A3," ITERATION END POINTS:     Y(LEFT) = ",  *
             F3.1,",  Y(RIGHT) = ",F3.1,/>,N,L,R);                 *

L2:          Y+(L+R)/2; FY+Y+3-12.6×Y+2+49.1×Y-58.5;   COUNT+COUNT+1; *
             IF FY=0 THEN GO TO L3;      IF ABS(R-Y)<@-8 THEN BEGIN  *
L3:          WRITE(LINE,<"ROOT FOUND ON THIS INTERVAL: Y = ",F8.6/>,Y*

             ); WRITE(LINE,<"NUMBER OF ITERATIONS USED:   ",I2//>,  *

             COUNT);   GO TO L1;  END;                             *
             FL+L+3-12.6×L+2+49.1×L-58.5; IF SIGN(FL)=-1 THEN GO TO L4*
             ELSE GO TO L5;                                       *
L4:          IF FY<0 THEN L+Y ELSE R+Y; GO TO L2;                 *
L5:          IF FY>0 THEN L+Y ELSE R+Y; GO TO L2;                 *
EOF:         WRITE(LINE,<"THE VALUES FOR Y GIVEN ABOVE ARE THE ROOTS "*
             "OF THE EQUATION;">); TIMER(0,LINE);                 *

          END.                                                     *
```

Figure 10.8   ALGOL *program for bisection approximation*

and is virtually assured to converge to a root. Endpoints for $y$ of 1 and 3, 3 and 5, and 5 and 7 were used in the program. The ALGOL program that was used to solve this problem is shown in Figure 10.8, and the results are shown in Figure 10.9. Based on the results given in the digital computer solution, we have, as the factored form of (10.12),

$$z = (y - 6.211636)(y - 4.080178)(y - 2.308186) \tag{10.20}$$

```
THIS IS AN EXTENDED ALGOL PROGRAM FOR COMPUTING THE
ROOTS OF A CUBIC EQUATION IN Y, USING THE BURROUGHS
B5500 COMPUTER.  THE ALGORITHM USED IS DERIVED FROM
THE BISECTION APPROXIMATION.

                                   3        2
THE POLYNOMIAL EQUATION IS:    Y  - 12.6Y  + 49.1Y - 58.5 = 0

1ST ITERATION END POINTS:      Y(LEFT) = 1.0, Y(RIGHT) = 3.0

ROOT FOUND ON THIS INTERVAL:   Y = 2.308186

NUMBER OF ITERATIONS USED:     28


2ND ITERATION END POINTS:      Y(LEFT) = 3.0, Y(RIGHT) = 5.0

ROOT FOUND ON THIS INTERVAL:   Y = 4.080178

NUMBER OF ITERATIONS USED:     28


3RD ITERATION END POINTS:      Y(LEFT) = 5.0, Y(RIGHT) = 7.0

ROOT FOUND ON THIS INTERVAL:   Y = 6.211636

NUMBER OF ITERATIONS USED:     28


THE VALUES FOR Y GIVEN ABOVE ARE THE ROOTS OF THE EQUATION.

****** TOTAL JOB TIME:           0 MIN    3.10 SEC ******
****** TOTAL PROCESSOR TIME:     0 MIN    0.52 SEC ******
****** TOTAL I/O TIME:           0 MIN    0.67 SEC ******
```

**Figure 10.9** *Printout of digital computer results*

These values were used as a standard in computing the percentage errors given for the results of the analog computer solution. The reader may note from the results (Figure 10.9) that the digital computer performed eighty-four iterations and obtained the results in a few seconds total job time. Furthermore, the digital computer was simultaneously working on other problems.

**10.2 summary**  The discussion and examples of this chapter have shown how analog computers can be used to solve algebraic equations. As mentioned, the analog computer is much slower than the digital computer in handling such equations. For the polynomial equation solved in Example 10.1, with the time scale factor of 10 as quoted, the analog computer required about 20 sec running time to obtain the plot shown in Figure 10.7. The digital computer solved the same equation in Example 10.2, to a higher degree of accuracy, in about 3 sec. This fact notwithstanding, we note that the analog computer can still do an acceptable job on a type of problem that it was not specifically designed to handle.

## PROBLEMS

10.1. Equation (10.12) may be written as

$$z = z_1 + z_2 + z_3 + z_4$$

An expression for $z_1$ is given by (10.13). Derive similar expressions for $z_2$, $z_3$, and $z_4$.

10.2. Confirm the initial conditions $x_{z_2}(0)$ and $x_{z_3}(0)$ as given by the settings of pots 6 and 7 in the final program of Example 10.1 (Figure 10.6).

10.3. Suppose a program such as the final one shown for Example 10.1 was used to find the *negative* real roots of a cubic equation like that of (10.12). Which initial conditions would change on the flow diagram shown for the example?

10.4. The characteristic equation of a system that is known to have all negative real roots is given by

$$Q = s^4 + 86s^3 + 2085s^2 + 14500s + 12500$$

The roots of this equation are to be found using the technique developed in this chapter. Assume one has determined that no roots occur for values of $s$ less than $-55$, suggest values for $s_N$ and $Q_N$.

10.5. One advantage of the technique for solving algebraic equations presented in this chapter is the ease with which solutions for varying coefficients can be determined. Suppose (10.12) was given as

$$z = y^3 - 10.5y^2 + 49.1y - 58.5$$

which pot or pots would have different settings from those shown in Figure 10.6? What would be the new value or values of the pot settings?

10.6.[2] Develop an analog computer flow diagram to solve the cubic equation

$$y = x^3 + 2.5x^2 + 1.8x + 1.2$$

on the interval $-2 \leq x \leq 2$.

10.7.[2] Develop an analog computer flow diagram to solve the quartic equation

$$y = x^4 + 1.1x^3 - 0.56x^2 + 0.86x + 1.20$$

on the interval $-2 \leq x \leq 0$.

10.8. Use the extended form of Descartes' rule of signs (see any introductory algebra test) to obtain as much information as possible about the number of positive, negative, and/or imaginary roots of the equation

$$y = 2x^5 + 4x^3 + 3x^2 - 1$$

---

[2] Problems 10.6 and 10.7 are taken from J. Forrest, "Simulating High-Order Algebraic Equations with Linear Analog Computer Elements," *Instruments and Control Systems*, Vol. 38, No. 3 (March 1965), 162–164.

# chapter eleven

Nearly all of the previous work in this text has dealt with analog computer solutions of typical linear differential equations. For most real physical systems of interest to scientists and engineers, the defining equation or equations are of an order greater than one. Techniques for scaling and programming these equations and for simulating system transfer functions were treated without regard to system order. The indirect programming technique (Section 3.1), for example, can be used with any $n$th-order linear (or nonlinear, for that matter) equation. The only real complexities that arise when using this programming technique are those associated with the increasing number of computing elements required for higher-order equations and the resulting increase in programming errors and computational inaccuracy that are likely to be introduced.

In this chapter, the *state variable* programming technique is introduced, and examples illustrate its application. To do this, we start in the next section with some background discussion of the state space concept. The state space approach to system analysis and synthesis is the subject matter of modern control theory; a subject that is significantly beyond the scope of this book. However, we present here a brief introduction, which yields techniques useful in the programming of nearly all system equations.

# state variable programming

The idea behind the *state* of a system is a very fundamental one and is, therefore, difficult if not impossible to define precisely. We propose to give an operational definition based on the *properties* required of a system whose behavior involves the notion of "state." The state of a system is defined to be the *minimum set of variables* that describes the present condition, or behavior, of the system. These variables are called the *state variables*, and for an $n$th-order system they are the $n$ components of the $n$-dimensional *state vector*. In many cases, the state variables may be rather arbitrarily chosen, but in every case they act as carriers of complete information about the transient state of the system. The state variables must contain sufficient information about the past history of the system in order to permit the computation of all future states of the system. As a consequence, all inputs and all describing equations must be known. For example, in a second-order mechanical system, the state variables $x_1$ and $x_2$ may define displacement and velocity, respectively. Then, $x_1(0)$ and $x_2(0)$ are the initial conditions that describe the initial state of the system. These numbers can then be used to compute the future state of the system $x_1(t)$ and $x_2(t)$, at some time $t$.

For most engineering problems associated with electromechanical or electrical systems, it is possible to relate the state variables of the system directly to the energy concept. The number of energy-storage elements within the system is exactly equal to the number of independent state variables, and the order or dimensionality of the system is therefore directly related to this number. Using this approach, it can be seen that any system is described by $n$ coupled first-order differential equations, rather than by *one* $n$th-order equation. This statement will be made clearer by the examples that follow.

**11.2 equation formulation and programming**

One of the very great advantages of the state variable approach to a problem is the systematic fashion in which defining system equations are presented. A complete discussion of this topic requires a background in matrix theory and manipulative techniques, which it is assumed that the average student reader of this text does not have. Furthermore, these techniques are really not appropriate material for an introductory text to analog computation, but they belong more properly within the purview of modern control theory. Our emphasis is to point out the ease with which a simple system of equations written in first-order, state variable form can be programmed on the analog computer.

*example 11.1*

As a first example showing the use of the state variable concept, we define the state variables for a simple second-order system, write the two defining first-order equations, and give the analog computer program for the equations. Consider the mechanical system shown in Example 3.1. The second-order equation given by (3.2) was

$$M\ddot{x} + B\dot{x} + Kx = Fu_{-1}(t) \tag{11.1}$$

where

$$
\begin{array}{llll}
M = & 2.00 \text{ kg} & K = & 1.28 \text{ N/m} \\
B = & 0.32 \text{ N-sec/m} & F = & 0.60 \text{ N}
\end{array}
\tag{11.2}
$$

$$\dot{x}(0) = -0.30 \text{ m/sec} \tag{11.3}$$

The choice of state variables for this system, as in many others, is quite arbitrary; there is no unique set. However, in view of energy considerations, it is appropriate to choose variables associated with the potential and kinetic energies of the system. On this basis, we may logically choose the displacement $x$ and the velocity $\dot{x}$ to be the two state variables. They are defined as

$$
\begin{aligned}
x_1 &\triangleq x \\
x_2 &\triangleq \dot{x}
\end{aligned}
\tag{11.4}
$$

Using (11.4) with (11.1), it is clear that one may write the two first-order defining relations as

$$\dot{x}_1 = x_2$$

$$\dot{x}_2 = \frac{F}{M} u_{-1}(t) - \frac{B}{M} x_2 - \frac{K}{M} x_1 \tag{11.5}$$

As pointed out earlier, an *n*th-order (in this case, second) equation is repre-sented in state-variable form as *n* (in this case, two) first-order equations.

The indirect programming technique applied to the two equations given by (11.5) is straightforward and results in the flow diagram shown in Figure 11.1. Pots 5 and 6 have been included in anticipation of the possibility of having to magnitude scale using the double-and-halve rule of Section 4.2. This flow

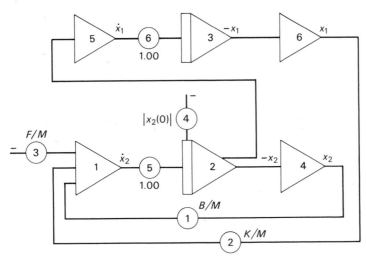

Figure 11.1

diagram was arranged as shown to illustrate the orderly solution of the two coupled equations. Amplifiers 5 and 6 are obviously not required since all they accomplish is a double sign inversion. All the pot settings are shown in terms of their literal values. If A5 and A6 are eliminated, the flow diagram shown in Figure 11.2 results. This flow diagram is clearly the same as the final

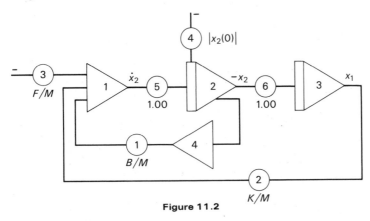

Figure 11.2

one (Figure 3.5) shown for Example 3.1 (which is fortuitous, in view of the fact that they both solve the same problem!).

Nothing has been said so far in this first example about scaling. From the programming standpoint one of the advantages of the state variable approach is that very simple magnitude scaling operations, such as the double-and-halve rule, can be used. This procedure, which can be termed "algebraic normaliza-tion," eliminates the requirement for the formal estimation of some maximum values. In the flow diagram of Figure 11.2, if the outside feedback loop is reduced to gain 1, the settings of the two integrator input pots can be made equal to the ratio of the system's natural frequency $\omega_n$ over the time scale factor $n$. This allows a very simple and quick choice of the time scale factor. Further, the setting of P1 can be made equal to the system damping ratio $\zeta$. The reader can confirm that adjusting the gains around A1 and A2 yields the flow diagram shown in Figure 11.3. Using the values given by (11.2), the pot settings are

$$P1 = 0.100 \qquad P5 = 0.800 \qquad n = 1.00$$
$$P3 = 0.469 \qquad P6 = 0.800$$
$$P4 = 0.375$$

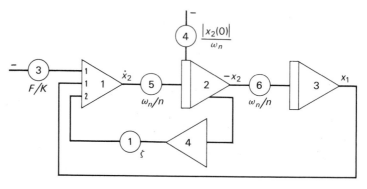

Figure 11.3

The solution for the state variable $x_1$ from this mechanization is the same as the solution for the original variable $x$ using the program of Example 3.1. This, of course, must be true, since the problem has a unique solution.

Example 11.1 illustrated the solution of a second-order system by programming two first-order equations. This example may have seemed somewhat artificial since the final analog program was no different from the one obtained by simply programming the original equation. However, our intention was to illustrate the technique and to show a simple application of the algebraic normalization procedure.

A more fundamental approach to a problem is to define the state variables directly from an idealized model and then to program the resulting first-order equations. If this approach is used, the state variables that are chosen probably differ from those selected if higher-order equations describing the system are written first. Energy considerations become more important here, as illustrated by the following example.

***example 11.2***

The electrical network shown in Figure 11.4, with the element values as given below, is designed to provide low pass filtering of the input:

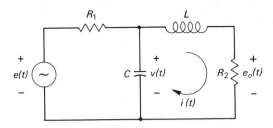

**Figure 11.4**

$$e(t) = 230 \sin 377t \qquad \begin{aligned} R_1 &= \phantom{0}500 \ \Omega \\ R_2 &= 4000 \ \Omega \end{aligned} \qquad \begin{aligned} L &= 20 \text{ H} \\ C &= 20 \ \mu\text{F} \end{aligned}$$

The analog computer programming of appropriate equations describing this filter is discussed in this example. These equations are written in state variable form, where the state variables are chosen based on fundamental energy considerations. The energies stored in the inductor and capacitor are given by

$$W_L = \tfrac{1}{2}Li^2 \tag{11.6}$$

$$W_C = \tfrac{1}{2}Cv^2 \tag{11.7}$$

The current $i$ and the voltage $v$ are as shown on the schematic diagram (Figure 11.4). Owing to the continuous nature of inductor currents and capacitor voltages, these variables can be chosen as state variables. They convey complete information about the transient state of the system, and any future state can thus be obtained from them.

In terms of the chosen state variables, the first-order coupled linear differential equations can be written as

$$C\frac{dv}{dt} = \frac{e - v}{R_1} - i \tag{11.8}$$

$$v = L\frac{di}{dt} + R_2 i \tag{11.9}$$

The functional dependence notation $v(t)$, $e(t)$, and $i(t)$ has been dropped for convenience. The equations above can be rewritten as

$$\dot{v} = -\frac{v}{R_1 C} - \frac{i}{C} + \frac{e}{R_1 C} \tag{11.10}$$

$$\dot{i} = -\frac{R_2 i}{L} + \frac{v}{L} \tag{11.11}$$

The notation $\dot{i}$ denotes the first derivative of the current with respect to time, likewise for $\dot{v}$. If the technique of algebraic normalization introduced in Example 11.1 is used, along with assumed normalizing constants $\dot{v}_N$, $v_N$, $e_N$, $\dot{i}_N$, and $i_N$, the following magnitude-scaled equations result:

$$\dot{x}_v = -\frac{v_N}{\dot{v}_N R_1 C} x_v - \frac{i_N}{\dot{v}_N C} x_i + \frac{e_N}{\dot{v}_N R_1 C} x_e \tag{11.12}$$

$$\dot{x}_i = -\frac{R_2 i_N}{L \dot{i}_N} x_i + \frac{v_N}{L \dot{i}_N} x_v \tag{11.13}$$

No attempt has been made yet to estimate the maximum value for any variable. These equations can be programmed in a manner that precludes the requirement for specifying all normalizing constants.

By properly grouping the terms in Equations (11.12) and (11.13), good passband time and magnitude scaling can be achieved quite easily. The time constants of both first-order equations appear explicitly, allowing a simple choice of a time scale factor. The equations may be written as

$$\dot{x}_v = \frac{1}{R_1 C} \frac{v_N}{\dot{v}_N} \left( -x_v - \frac{R_1 i_N}{v_N} x_i + \frac{e_N}{v_N} x_e \right) \tag{11.14}$$

$$\dot{x}_i = \frac{R_2}{L} \frac{i_N}{\dot{i}_N} \left( -x_i + \frac{v_N}{R_2 i_N} x_v \right) \tag{11.15}$$

Since we are dealing with normalized variables, there is the usual requirement to consider integrator input pots set to the ratio of normalizing constants. A literal partial program for (11.14) can thus be shown (but not actually wired) as given in Figure 11.5. The setting of P2a is, of course, due simply to the usual

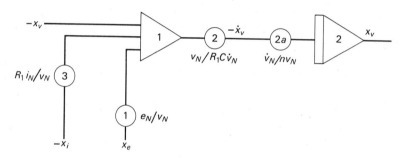

**Figure 11.5**

normalization procedure and a recognition that time scaling is required. The gain on A2 is the product of the settings of P2 and P2a and is simply $1/nR_1 C$. Similarly, it is easy to show that the integrator required to program (11.15) has a gain equal to

$$\frac{1}{n(L/R_2)} \tag{11.16}$$

Thus, in the programming of (11.14) and (11.15), the two time constants $R_1 C$ and $L/R_2$ appear explicitly in the integrator gains. The choice of a time scale factor $n$ is very easy and specifying $\dot{v}_N$ or $\dot{i}_N$ is not required. The only normalizing constants to be chosen are $e_N$, $i_N$, $v_N$, and $e_{oN}$. The normalizing constant $e_{oN}$ is required since the output voltage $e_o(t)$ of the filter must appear in the program.

The flow diagram shown in Figure 11.6 represents a mechanization of the equations describing the low pass filter of this example. The pot settings are all shown in terms of the literal coefficients in Equations (11.14) and (11.15), reflecting the previous discussion regarding integrator gains. The forcing function (voltage source input) is shown in scaled form as a normalized variable; it is

$$x_e \triangleq \frac{e}{e_N} = \frac{1}{e_N} (230 \sin 377t) \tag{11.17}$$

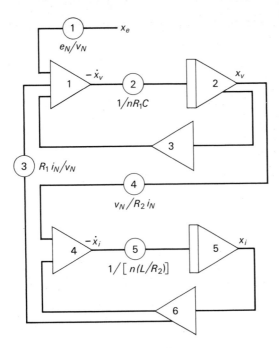

**Figure 11.6**

In order to calculate pot settings in this program it is necessary to specify those normalizing constants that appear in the program. Assuming low-frequency operation of the filter, one can conservatively choose

$$v_N = e_N = e_{oN} = 250 \text{ V} \tag{11.18}$$

Since, from the filter circuit,

$$e_o = R_2 i \tag{11.19}$$

we can choose

$$i_N = \frac{e_{oN}}{R_2} = \frac{250}{4000} = 0.0625 \text{ A} \tag{11.20}$$

Using these results, the output voltage $e_o(t)$ can be normalized as follows:

$$x_{e_o} = \frac{e_o}{e_{oN}} = \frac{R_2 i}{e_{oN}} = \frac{R_2 i_N}{e_{oN}} x_i = x_i \tag{11.21}$$

This result does not imply that the output voltage is the same as the loop current! It does mean that, with proper interpretation of the results, both these quantities can be obtained from the output of A5.

Using (11.18) with (11.17), the normalized input becomes

$$x_e = 0.920 \sin 377t \tag{11.22}$$

The setting $e_N/v_N$ of P1 is unity. However, P1 can be set to 0.920 to account for the reduced sinusoidal input given by (11.22). With this one modification, the pot settings in the program for this example are

$$\begin{array}{lll} \text{P1} = 0.920 & \text{P4} = 1.000 & n = 1000 \\ \text{P2} = 0.100 & \text{P5} = 0.200 & \\ \text{P3} = 0.125 & & \end{array}$$

The integrator input pots in the sine-cosine generator required to complete this example would be set to $\omega/n$, or 0.377.

The above example illustrated the use of the state variable approach in the analog computer programming of a simple electrical network. The state variables, chosen directly from energy considerations, resulted in two simple linear equations. The algebraic normalization employed resulted in relatively easy magnitude and time scaling.

**11.3 summary**

This chapter, because it was meant to be only an introductory treatment of the subject, was concerned mainly with the writing, scaling, and programming of simple linear first-order equations written around the state space concept. The state space approach to linear system theory, using matrix notation and manipulations, is a highly systematic means of analysis. The interested reader is encouraged to consult any of the fine texts in modern control theory for a unified treatment of this important new area.

A few summarizing comments about the state space approach should be mentioned. They are

(a) An $n$th-order linear or nonlinear differential equation can be expressed as $n$ first-order equations. This resulting system of coupled equations is generally easier to solve than the original $n$th-order equation, particularly if electronic computers are available.

(b) The state variable concept allows the investigator to easily observe intermediate states of a dynamic system, not just the input and output states.

(c) The state variable formulation of a nonlinear differential equation is usually not much more difficult than the writing of a linear equation. Thus, this approach allows an orderly and systematic approach to all systems. The use of matrix notation allows great flexibility in analysis.

(d) Multivariable systems having several inputs and/or outputs can be easily handled in state variable form. Conventional transfer function techniques cannot be utilized in such a case.

(e) Since nonconstant-coefficient first-order differential equations can be programmed quite easily, the state space technique allows a systematic approach to time varying systems.

(f) Magnitude and time scaling of state variable equations is greatly simplified, which results in easier analog computer programming.

## PROBLEMS

11.1. How are the energies in the system of Example 11.1 related to the choice of state variables that was made?

11.2. The final flow diagram (Figure 11.3) for Example 11.1 was obtained by first multiplying-and-dividing around A1 and then dividing-and-multiplying around A2. (Actually, the multiplying of the A2 output was done at pots 1 and 6.) Determine the two factors by which the gains were adjusted, in terms of the constants $M$ and $K$ of the system. Why did the setting of pot 4 change?

11.3. If the outputs of amplifiers 1 and 2 in the final programs shown for Examples 3.1 and 11.1 were plotted using the same plotter sensitivities, would the two graphs be identical? If not, what interpretation would have to be made, and why?

11.4. For the low pass filter of Example 11.2, show that the voltage transfer ratio can be written in the form

$$G(s) = \frac{E_o(s)}{E(s)}$$

$$= \left(\frac{R_2}{R_1 + R_2}\right)\left(\frac{\omega_n^2}{s^2 + 2\zeta\omega_n s + \omega_n^2}\right)$$

where

$$\omega_n^2 = \frac{R_1 + R_2}{R_1 CL}$$

$$\zeta = \frac{R_1 R_2 C + L}{2R_1 CL\omega_n}$$

11.5. Using the results of Problem 11.4, predict the attenuation, in decibels, of the filter for sinusoidal inputs whose radian frequencies are

10, 150, and 377 rad/sec

11.6. Show that in the programming of (11.15) an integrator gain as given by relation (11.16) is required.

11.7. The sketch in Figure 11.7 shows an electromechanical model of a dc motor.

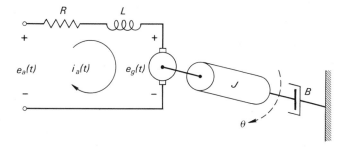

**Figure 11.7**

$J$ is the motor armature moment of inertia, and $B$ represents a rotational damping constant. The armature circuit inductance and resistance are as shown.

The basic motor relations are given by

$$T \text{ (mechanical torque)} = K_T i_a$$

$$e_g(t) \text{ (emf)} = K_g \dot{\theta}$$

(a) Write two differential equations (one of second-order) with $i_a$ and $\theta$ as dependent variables.

(b) Choose as state variables $\theta$, $\dot{\theta}$, and $i_a$ and write three state-variable first-order equations.

(c) Comment on the choice of state variables given in part (b) in terms of the energies of the system.

11.8. In Problem 11.7, choose as state variables $\theta$, $\dot{\theta}$, and $\ddot{\theta}$ and write the three first-order equations.

*Note:* The following two problems involve the use of matrix theory in the handling of state variable equations. They are included here to illustrate simply the basic technique, and can be attempted by students having some familiarity with matrix manipulation.

11.9. A system of first-order, state variable equations may be represented in matrix form by

$$\dot{\bar{x}} = A\bar{x} + B\bar{u}$$

where

$\bar{x} = n$-dimensional *state vector*, whose column elements are the state variables

$A = $ *coefficient matrix*

$B = $ *distribution matrix*

$\bar{u} = $ *control vector*

Using this notation, the state variable Equations (11.5) of Example 11.1 may be written as

$$\begin{bmatrix} \dot{x}_1 \\ \dot{x}_2 \end{bmatrix} = \begin{bmatrix} 0 & 1 \\ -K/M & -B/M \end{bmatrix} \begin{bmatrix} x_1 \\ x_2 \end{bmatrix} + \begin{bmatrix} 0 & 0 \\ 1/M & 0 \end{bmatrix} \begin{bmatrix} Fu_{-1}(t) \\ 0 \end{bmatrix}$$

Following this example, represent Equations (11.10) and (11.11) in the above form.

11.10. The following is a vector-matrix representation of a system of three state variable equations derived from one third-order equation (as the system (11.5) was derived from (11.1)):

$$
\begin{bmatrix} \dot{x}_1 \\ \dot{x}_2 \\ \dot{x}_3 \end{bmatrix} = \begin{bmatrix} 0 & 1 & 0 \\ 0 & 0 & 1 \\ -6 & -11 & -6 \end{bmatrix} \begin{bmatrix} x_1 \\ x_2 \\ x_3 \end{bmatrix} + \begin{bmatrix} 0 & 0 & 0 \\ 0 & 0 & 0 \\ 3 & 2 & 0 \end{bmatrix} \begin{bmatrix} u \\ \dot{u} \\ 0 \end{bmatrix}
$$

If the state variables were chosen to be equal to the following:

$$
\begin{bmatrix} x_1 \\ x_2 \\ x_3 \end{bmatrix} = \begin{bmatrix} y \\ \dot{y} \\ \ddot{y} \end{bmatrix}
$$

find the original third-order differential equation in $y$.

# appendix A

**A.0 introduction**

We discuss briefly the physical arrangement and operation of the TR-20 desk top analog computer, manufactured by Electronic Associates, Inc., Long Branch, New Jersey. This is a modern, solid state computer that, in its fully expanded configuration, is capable of performing all mathematical operations required in the solution of most scientific and engineering problems. The TR-20 has available twenty amplifiers and twenty potentiometers, together with integrator networks, multipliers, other nonlinear components, and associated support systems.

This particular computer is typical of a general class of small desk top computers built by various manufacturers. The computer techniques discussed in this text are general, however, and are not written for any particular type of analog computing equipment. The material in this appendix has been included as an aid to the many students or engineers who may have the TR-20 analog computer available. For this machine, or any other, an operator's manual should always be consulted before any machine operation is attempted. A similar comment applies for the particular strip chart recorder discussed in Section A.5. Most manufacturers of analog computers will supply operator's manuals on request.

# computer operation

The TR-20 computer (Figure A.1) is arranged in three vertical rows, or sections, below which is a sloping control panel area. The uppermost section contains the dual attenuator (potentiometer) units (number 42.187). Each unit contains two pots, numbered from top to bottom, with the numbers appearing on the frame member directly beneath each unit. The middle section contains the dual integrator networks (number 12.1116), the multipliers (number 7.045), the reference networks (number 12.266), the display panel, and any other nonlinear components. The bottom vertical panel contains the dual dc operational amplifier units (number 6.712). Each unit, or panel, contains two amplifiers, numbered from top to bottom, with the numbers appearing on the frame member directly above each amplifier panel.

**A.1 general layout**

The computer is usually equipped with a removable patch board. The computing elements are interconnected with a set of color coded patch wires and special purpose plugs (commonly called "bottle plugs"). Care must be exercised in removing the patch wires to prevent internal open or intermittent open circuits. The patch wires should be handled by grasping the heavy molded portion near the plug; multiple connectors are available for joining two or more patch wires.

**Figure A.1** *TR-20 computer and strip recorder*

The sloping control panel area contains the power controls, overload warning system, pot setting controls, readout facilities, and mode control switch. A photograph of the control panel is shown in Figure A.2. The primary function of each control is:

| | | |
|---|---|---|
| S4 | Power switch | Controls application of primary ac power to the computer. The voltmeter M1 is illuminated when S4 is in the ON position. |
| S5 | Mode control switch | Controls the operational mode of the computer. Rocker-type switch with positions of RESET, HOLD, and OPERATE. The RESET position is also referred to as the initial condition (IC) position. |

| S1 | Voltmeter function switch | Controls voltmeter M1 operation. Positions are POT BUS, NULL, VM, AMPL, and BAL. We are not concerned with the BAL position, and with J1 connected to J2 (our usual case) the VM and AMPL positions are equivalent. |
| --- | --- | --- |
| S2 | Voltmeter range switch | Selects voltmeter sensitivity. Full range of the scale is 0.1, 0.3, 1, 3, 10, and 30 V. This control is normally left on the 10 setting. |
| S3 | Null pot and reference selector switch | Used with the voltmeter to set pots and measure amplifier outputs by the null comparison method. |
| S6 | Amplifier selector switch | Used to select any installed amplifier for output reading and/or recording. |
| R10 | Null pot | A precision calibrated 10-turn potentiometer. Used for setting the pots and measuring amplifier outputs by the null comparison method. |
| DS1 | Overload indicators | Indicate overloads of those amplifiers whose numbers are illuminated. |

The mode control switch, S5 in Figure A.2, can start and stop computer problem solutions and establish initial conditions on integrators. The switch

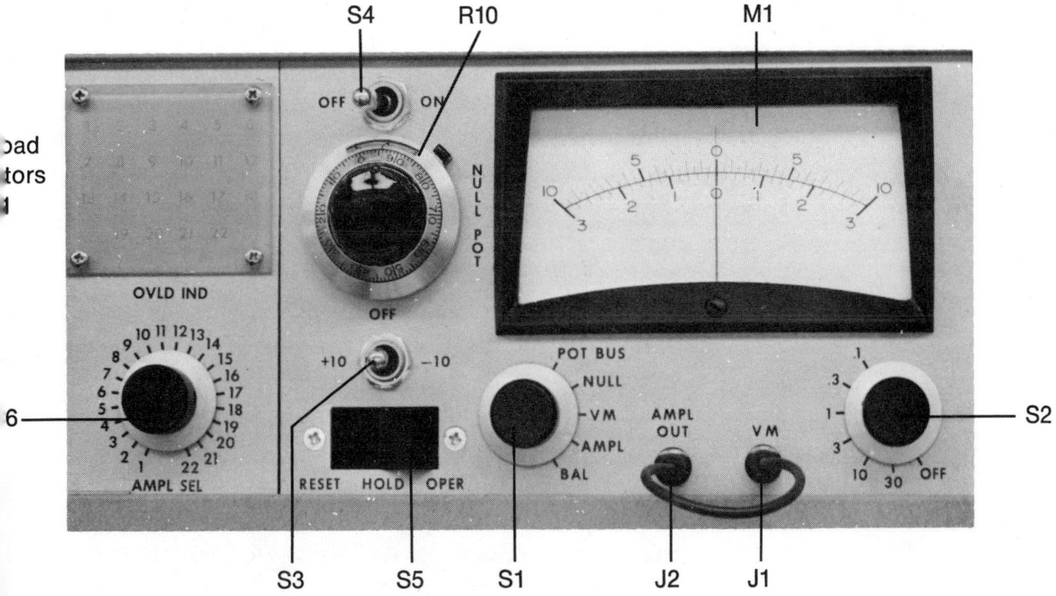

**A.2 mode control**

Figure A.2 *TR-20 control panel*

positions are RESET (or IC), HOLD, and OPER (operate). All computing components, *except* amplifiers connected as integrators, are operational in each of the three modes. This switch is left in the RESET mode during problem wiring and also at all other times when the actual problem solution is not being run. The switch is moved through the HOLD mode to OPER when the solution is to be observed or plotted. The HOLD position is used when the solution is to be interrupted for making an output reading. The HOLD is also used on occasion to interrupt the problem solution for a short time; when the switch is again moved to OPER the solution continues.

The integrators function in the various computer modes in the following manner:

RESET

The output voltages of the integrators are set to the values required by the initial conditions of the problem. All other inputs to the integrators are disconnected in this mode. This means, for example, that if an IC of $+0.133$ is present on an integrator then the only output possible in the RESET mode is a constant of $-0.133$ (the sign is always inverted). The static check (Chapter 5) is calculated assuming the computer is in the RESET mode.

HOLD

The inputs to the integrators are removed, integration stops, and all variables are held at the values present when the switch was moved from OPER to HOLD.

OPER

The integrators receive the inputs as patched on the computer wiring panel, and integration with respect to time (as defined by relation (2.26)) takes place.

**A.3 pot wiring and setting**

In Section 2.1 we discussed the use of potentiometers for the multiplication of variables by positive constants less than unity. In this section we discuss the actual wiring (or patching) of the TR-20 pots and explain how to set the pots to the desired coefficients. The pots are installed in the top section on the vertical front of the machine. A typical dual unit is shown in Figure A.3 (page 143).

The input and output jacks (holes) for pot 1 (or P1) are located on the lower left side of the panel. The value to which P1 is adjusted depends upon the setting of knob R1. Note that the pot control R1 does not have a calibrated dial. The pot has a 10-turn range but, due to a built in override clutch, it can be turned continuously in either the clockwise or the counterclockwise direction. The small pushbutton switches S1-(a,b) and S2-(a,b) are used in the pot setting procedure. We will discuss the setting of the pot after we see how it is patched into our problem.

The schematic for each pot is shown on the attenuator panel. All odd numbered pots have their "low" ends grounded internally and this terminal does not appear at a jack. The even numbered pots are *not* grounded internally but their low ends may be grounded by inserting the light-colored plug shown in the lower portion of Figure A.3. As mentioned in Section 2.1, we usually use all pots such that the low end must be grounded. Thus, we leave the bottle plug installed. The top hole associated with each pot schematic is the *input*, and the middle hole (the wiper arm or sliding contact) is the *output* jack. Referring to Figure 2.1, we see that the input $x_i$ would be patched into the *top* hole, and the output $Kx_i$ would be obtained from the *center* hole. In many cases (initial conditions for example), the input to the pot comes from positive or negative computer reference. In this case we would patch from the appropriate $+10$ or $-10$ hole on the reference networks (number 12.266).

As shown in Section 2.1, all pots must be set under load. This requires that the pot output (middle hole) be patched to the appropriate gain 1 or gain 10 input on the amplifier that follows the pot. If the load is changed, then the pot must be reset. The actual setting procedure is outlined in the following steps. For simplicity, the switches and controls referred to are as described on Figures A.2 and A.3.

| | |
|---|---|
| Step 1 | Provide the proper load for the pot to be set; this is usually an amplifier input resistor. *DO NOT* load one pot with another (or with a recorder), because under such a situation a correct setting cannot be achieved. |
| Step 2 | Place S5 in the RESET mode. |
| Step 3 | Rotate S1 to the POT BUS position. |
| Step 4 | Throw S3 to the $+10$ position. |
| Step 5 | Set the precision null pot R10 to the desired setting. Three-place accuracy is assured and the fourth place can be interpolated to about plus or minus two digits. Do not rotate the small locking lever behind R10; it is to remain in the full counterclockwise direction. |
| Step 6 | Depress the readout switch S1-(a,b) (which is associated with the pot being set), and hold it in this position. |
| Step 7 | Rotate the appropriate pot knob R1 *in the direction that the needle on the voltmeter* M1 *must move* to reach zero (that is, midscale). Continue rotating R1 until the needle reaches zero on M1. When the needle rests over zero, the pot is adjusted to the exact value set on the precision null pot R10. |

This technique utilizes the null comparison method. Close adherence to the above sequence of steps assures accurate pot settings. It should be emphasized again that pots *must* be set under load and, if the load is changed, the pot must be reset.

When the pots in an actual problem are being set, one may observe an overload condition for one or more of the amplifiers on the overload indicator panel. This is very undesirable and can result in damaging an amplifier. This can sometimes be rectified by:

(1) turning the knobs on all pots used in the problem to zero (full counter-clockwise until the override clutch engages) *before* the computer is even turned on; or

(2) setting first those pots that, because of their function in the particular problem, are causing the overload(s).

The latter technique usually requires a good deal of insight into the problem.

Finally, as a time-saving convenience, it is desirable to arrange the order of setting the pots according to ascending (or descending) magnitudes. This eliminates much adjusting of the null pot R10.

## A.4 amplifier wiring and readout

The TR-20 amplifier units (number 6.712) are located in the lower section of the vertical front portion of the computer. They may be wired in those configurations discussed in Sections 2.4 and 2.5. Figure A.4 shows one dual amplifier unit.

The left-hand rows of holes are the amplifier inputs (gain 1 or gain 10 as shown); the right-hand holes are the outputs. The solid lines represent internal connections. SJ refers to the summing junction, and B and O represent the high-gain amplifier input and output, respectively. (Note the use of the small high-gain amplifier symbol.)

The bottle plug, which protrudes outwards in Figure A.4, should be installed for the operational amplifier to function as an inverter (one gain 1 input), coefficient amplifier (one gain 10 input), or summer (several inputs). This plug simply shorts SJ to B and connects the top resistor as feedback between O and SJ. Thus the amplifier is depicted as shown in Figure 2.7. We have two gain 1 and two gain 10 inputs available. If additional inputs are required one may "borrow" a bank of input resistors from an unused amplifier. To do this, remove the bottle plug on the borrowed amplifier, short B to O, and then connect the SJ points together on the two amplifiers. The input resistors on the borrowed amplifier are now available as additional inputs to the first amplifier, giving us five gain 1 and four gain 10 inputs.

To use the amplifier as an integrator, remove the bottle plug and connect the SJ, B, and O holes to the corresponding holes on the integrator network (number 12.1116), which is located in the front center section. One now has three gain 1 inputs, two gain 10 inputs, and six output holes. The initial condition is patched to the IC hole in the integrator network.

The output of any amplifier may be read on the voltmeter by rotating switch S6 (indicated in Figure A.2) to the number of the desired amplifier. If switch S1 is set on AMPL (or VM, if J2 is connected to J1), the meter reads the output of the amplifier. If the computer is switched to the HOLD mode (switch S5), a fairly accurate meter reading can be made. However, a more accurate technique is to use the null comparison method similar to that used in setting pots. To do this, we must again "address" the proper amplifier with S6. The

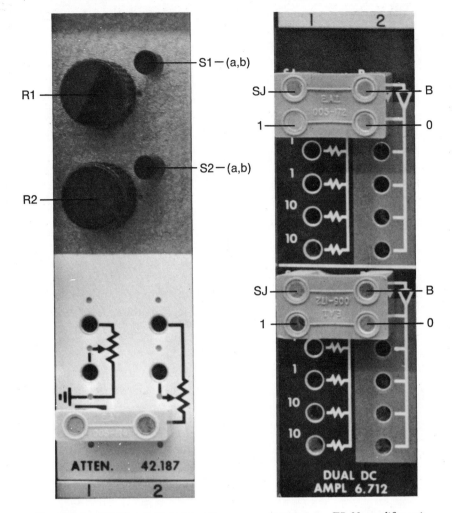

**Figure A.3**  *TR-20 potentiometer unit*          **Figure A.4**  *TR-20 amplifier unit*

computer must be switched to the HOLD mode and switch S1 should be in the AMPL position. At this point, the output of the desired amplifier appears on the meter, as discussed above. Now, however, we simply note whether the output as shown on M1 is positive or negative. We then throw switch S3 to +10 or −10, according to whether the observed output is plus or minus. Now, switch S1 is moved to the NULL position. The null pot R10 is then turned in the correct direction to cause the needle on the panel voltmeter M1 to reach midscale (or zero). When M1 is zeroed, we can read the normalized output (a number between 0 and 1) on the dial of R10. The sign is, of course, the same as the polarity to which we set switch S3. Using this technique, three-place accuracy in reading is assured and the fourth place can be interpolated to within about plus or minus two digits.

One graphic recording device that can be used with the TR-20 computer is the model S-601-S, Speed Servo strip recorder manufactured by the Esterline Angus Instrument Co., Inc., Indianapolis, Indiana. This is a portable, single

**A.5 recorder operation**

channel device that produces an ink recording on rectilinear paper moving under the writing pen. We use the strip recorder to plot solutions of the problems solved on the computer. The recorder input comes from the particular amplifier whose output is the desired variable. A separate recorder connector cable can be used to wire the input to the back of the $Y_1$ jack on the computer display panel. This panel is located in the center section of the vertical computer front area. Thus, we need only patch from the particular amplifier whose output we wish to plot to the $Y_1$ jack on the display panel. This connection should be taken through any unused inverting amplifier in order to compensate for the fact that the recorder normally experiences a "downward" (below the zero axis) deflection for all positive signals.

The recorder operating controls are shown in Figure A.5. The primary function of each recorder control is:

| | | |
|---|---|---|
| S1 | Power switch | Controls application of ac power to the recorder. When the recorder power supply is plugged into the receptacle at the rear of the computer, this switch is ineffective until the *computer* power switch is ON. |
| I1 | Power *on* indicator | Illuminated when power is being delivered to the recorder. |
| S3 | Zero switch | Used to zero the recording pen. The pen should rest over the center of the recording chart when properly zeroed. When adjusting this control, S4 should be turned OFF and/or the input signal should be removed. S3 should be locked when a proper adjustment is obtained. |
| S4 | Range switch | During normal operation, this switch is *always* positioned at the 10 V position. This means that an amplifier output of $\pm 10$ V (corresponding to a normalized $\pm 1$ output) provides full-scale deflection for the recording pen. |
| S2 | Chart feed rate (paper speed) selector | Controls the rate at which the recording chart moves under the writing pen. Positions are 0.75, 1.5, 3, 6, and 12 *inches per minute*. This control may be changed while the paper is in motion, if necessary. |
| I2 | Chart supply indicator | Provides a visual indication of the amount of chart paper remaining on the roll in the recorder. |

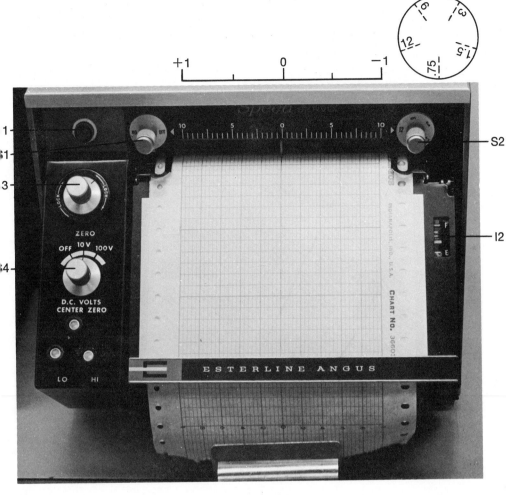

**Figure A.5** *Strip recorder control panel*

Although a chart paper rewind roller is provided in the recorder, we generally do not use it. Rather, we simply allow the paper to unwind under the "tearing bar" on the bottom front writing panel, then individual records can be torn off as the solution progresses. A 6-oz weight must be attached to the free end of the recording paper to provide sufficient tension over the notched drive wheels. The notched black thumb wheel located on the right-hand side of the drive roller may be used to manually advance the record. The chart paper used with the recorder is 103 ft long. Since we may sometimes operate at a speed of 12 in./min, the paper supply could last for as short a time as $\sim 100$ min. Students should not attempt to change paper rolls or to refill the ink supply unless they have been shown the proper method for doing this.

# appendix B

The precision diode circuits mentioned in Chapter 8 are listed and discussed here. These circuits are necessary for mechanizing some nonlinearities commonly encountered in systems analysis, including such functions as rectification, limiting, dead zone, etc. For every such function, the circuit is shown, the transfer characteristic is defined, and a very brief discussion of the setup procedures is included.

There are many types of diode circuits that have been developed to mechanize the almost unlimited number of nonlinearities that must be dealt with. The introductory analytical techniques introduced in Chapter 8 should allow the reader to devise a precision diode circuit to generate nearly any transfer characteristic desired. The development of a more sophisticated transfer characteristic can often be thought of as the superposed sum of several basic transfer characteristics. This building block approach suggests combining several basic diode circuits to generate the desired characteristic. Many different types of complex transfer characteristics can be generated using the basic circuits given here. The use of these diode circuits with the analog computer enables the student or engineer to analyze or design nonlinear systems without the necessity of making linearizing approximations. As a result, the range of problems that can be handled is greatly increased and the validity of the solu-

# precision diode circuits

tions is enhanced. Furthermore, an extensive knowledge of classical nonlinear analytical techniques is not required.

The diode circuit is shown in Figure B.1. Note that in this circuit, as in the others in this appendix, a new notation has been introduced. The gain 1 indicated for the two inputs to the high-gain amplifier means that the amplifier is set up such that the normal gain 1 input resistor is connected between the two inputs and SJ. It does *not* mean the same thing as gain 1 does in the case of an operational amplifier, as discussed in Section 2.4. It is simply a convenient way to represent the two resistors $R_i$ and $R_f$ as shown for the circuit of Example 8.2. The transfer characteristic for the circuit of Figure B.1 is shown in Figure B.2.

The diodes in Figure B.1 can be reversed to yield a clamped output for all positive inputs and an inverted output for all negative inputs. Furthermore, such basic circuits can be used, as mentioned in Section B.0, as building blocks for more complicated transfer characteristics.

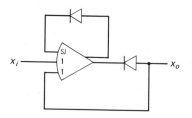

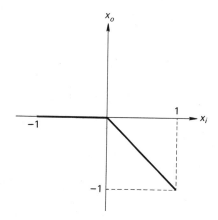

Figure B.1 *Precision halfwave rectifier circuit*

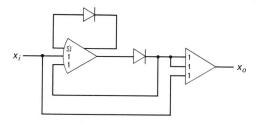

Figure B.2 *Halfwave rectifier transfer characteristic*

A precision diode circuit that can be used to accomplish fullwave rectification is commonly called an absolute value circuit and is shown in Figure B.3. Note that the second amplifier is set up as a normal summer. The notation associated with the first amplifier is as discussed in Section B.1. The transfer characteristic obtained from this circuit is shown in Figure B.4. Note that $x_o = -|x_i|$. In order to obtain $x_o = +|x_i|$, we need only reverse both diodes.

Figure B.3 *Precision fullwave rectifier circuit*

The diode circuit is shown in Figure B.5. The transfer characteristic obtained from this circuit is shown in Figure B.6. The pot shown on the flow diagram is connected in the usual manner and is set to the value desired for the normalized magnitude of the limited output. The output can be limited for all negative

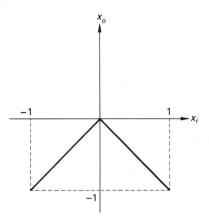

**Figure B.4**   *Fullwave rectifier transfer characteristic*

inputs if the diodes are reversed and a positive computer reference voltage is applied as the input of the pot.

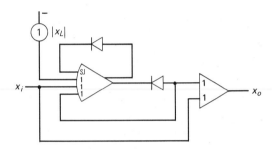

**Figure B.5**   *Precision single-side limiter circuit*

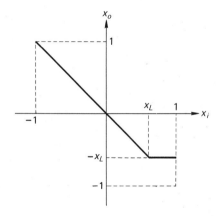

**Figure B.6**   *Single-side limiter transfer characteristic*

The precision dual side limiter circuit is obtained by combining the single-side limiter circuits discussed in Section B.3. It is shown in Figure B.7, and its transfer characteristic is shown in Figure B.8. The pots in Figure B.7 are set to the values that the normalized output is limited to. The settings of the pots need not be the same. The gain of the dual-side limiter in the linear region

**B.4 dual-side limiter**

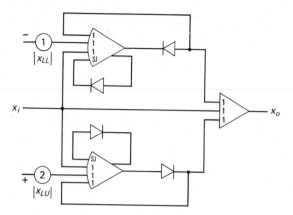

**Figure B.7** *Precision dual-side limiter circuit*

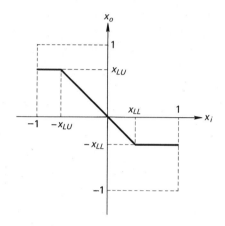

**Figure B.8** *Dual-side limiter transfer characteristic*

can be changed from unity to some value $K$ by using three gain-$K$ inputs on the final summer and by dividing the pot settings by the same $K$.

**B.5**
**SIGN**
**function**

A special diode circuit is used to generate a function that is frequently referred to in systems analysis as the SIGN or SGN function. Such a function has the following property:

$$\text{SIGN(arg)} = +1, \text{ for arg} > 0$$
$$\text{SIGN(arg)} = \phantom{+}0, \text{ for arg} = 0 \tag{B.1}$$
$$\text{SIGN(arg)} = -1, \text{ for arg} < 0$$

The analog computer mechanization of this function employs a circuit that is essentially equivalent to Equation (B.1), except that for zero input the output is not identically equal to zero. Instead, the output is undefined for zero input but it lies in the range between plus and minus one. The SIGN function is useful in computation for representing nonlinearities such as Coulomb friction and for generating arbitrary forcing functions.

The diode circuit used to generate the SIGN function is basically a modification of the dual-side limiter discussed in Example 8.2. It may be thought of as being a dual-side limiter having infinite gain in the region before limiting occurs. One such circuit is as shown in Figure B.9.

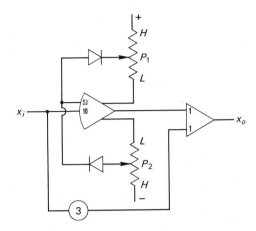

**Figure B.9**  *Precision* SIGN *function circuit*

Pots P1 and P2 are ungrounded pots and are connected and adjusted as discussed in Example 8.2. Pot P3 is set to a very small value, usually of the order of about 0.1. This pot is used only to cancel the "softness" of the two diodes, thereby yielding a transfer characteristic with zero slope in the limited regions. Figure B.10 shows the transfer characteristic of the SIGN function circuit.

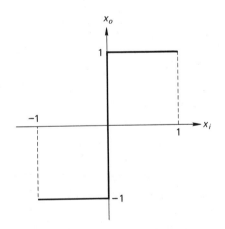

**Figure B.10**  SIGN *function transfer characteristic*

It is clearly a mechanization of the function described by relation (B.1), except for the undefined output for zero inputs.

Another nonlinearity commonly encountered in nature is the dead zone, or dead space, phenomenon. This function can best be illustrated by considering the transfer characteristic shown in Figure B.11. Such a function might be needed, for example, to describe the forces in a mechanical system in which a

**B.6
dead-zone
function**

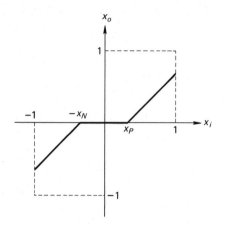

**Figure B.11**  *Dead-zone transfer characteristic*

body was free to move between certain limits (scaled to $x_N$ and $x_P$) before restraining forces were applied or encountered.

A precision dead-zone diode circuit is shown in Figure B.12. The pots

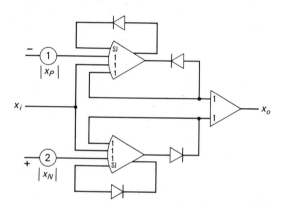

**Figure B.12**  *Precision dead-zone circuit*

are set to the values $x_N$ and $x_P$; that is, their settings determine the width of the dead zone. These settings clearly do not have to be equal in magnitude. Also, the gain in the regions where output occurs does not have to be unity as shown in Figure B.11. A slope equal to $K$ can be achieved by using two gain-$K$ inputs to the final summer. However, referring to Figure B.11, it should be clear that high gains on the final summer could, if due care is not taken, result in serious overloads.

The six precision diode circuits listed in this appendix are typical examples of the type of circuit used to generate arbitrary transfer characteristics. Other examples of such circuits can be found in any text on analog computation. Further, the basic circuits described here can frequently be employed to form more sophisticated functions by superposition. The various outputs of the individual diode circuits need only be summed to yield transfer characteristics that are the graphical sum of those generated by the individual circuits.

Finally, the comments regarding scaling made in Section 8.3 must be reemphasized here. The transfer characteristics given in this appendix are all labeled in terms of normalized variables. As always, the basic constraint is that no amplifier can have an output greater than plus or minus unity.

# appendix C

**C.0
introduction**  The ten laboratory exercises in this appendix are typical of the kinds of engineering problems that can easily be solved using the analog computer. The student should be prepared to solve many of these problems after having studied the sections covering programming and magnitude and time scaling. All exercises involve magnitude scaling, including the requirement to estimate maximum values. All except Laboratory Numbers 1, 2, and 8 require time scaling. Multipliers are needed in Laboratory Numbers 5 and 7, and diode circuits are used in Laboratory Numbers 8 and 10. The order of difficulty is not necessarily the same as the order of presentation; Laboratory Numbers 1, 2, 4, 5, and 7 are probably less difficult than the other Laboratory exercises.

**lab no. 1
steering
linkage**  Figure C.1 shows an idealized model of the rotary mechanical system acting as the load on a ship steering motor. The moments of inertia $J$, damping constant (dashpot) $B$, and stiffness constant (spring) $K$ represent the rudder, gearing, shafts, bearings, etc. This is a two-degrees-of-freedom system, where the displacement angles $\theta_1$ and $\theta_2$ are chosen as shown. $T_a(t)$ represents a step function torque applied by the motor.

**154   laboratory exercises**

Lab.#1

$$\left(\frac{J_1 J_2}{B}\right)\dddot{\theta}_2 + (J_1 + J_2)\ddot{\theta}_2 + \left(\frac{J_1 k}{B}\right)\dot{\theta}_2 + K\theta_2 = T_a U_{-1}(t)$$

$$250\,\dddot{\theta} + 1156.25\,\ddot{\theta} + 1100\,\dot{\theta} + 1562.5\theta = 92,500\, U_{-1}(t)$$

I.C. : $\ddot{\theta}(0) = -40$

$\dot{\theta}(0) = 82.5$

$\theta(0) = 0$

magnitude scaling

$$250\,\frac{\dddot{\theta}_N}{\theta}\left(\frac{\dddot{\theta}}{\dddot{\theta}_N}\right) + 1156.25\,\ddot{\theta}_N\left(\frac{\ddot{\theta}}{\ddot{\theta}_N}\right) + 1100\dot{\theta}_N\left(\frac{\dot{\theta}}{\dot{\theta}_N}\right) + 1562.5\theta_N\left(\frac{\theta}{\theta_N}\right) = 92,500\, U_{-1}(t)$$

$$\ddot{x}_\theta + \left|\frac{1156.25}{250}\frac{\ddot{\theta}_N}{\dddot{\theta}_N}\right|\ddot{x}_\theta + \left(\frac{1100}{250}\frac{\dot{\theta}_N}{\ddot{\theta}_N}\right)\dot{x}_\theta + \left(\frac{1562.5}{250}\frac{\theta_N}{\dddot{\theta}_N}\right)x_\theta = \left(\frac{92500}{250\,\dddot{\theta}_N}\right)U_{-1}(t)$$

$\frac{92500}{250\,\dddot{\theta}_N} \overset{SET}{=} 1 \to \dddot{\theta}_N = 370 \overset{Quess}{\to 500}$

$\frac{1156.25}{250}\left(\frac{\ddot{\theta}_N}{\dddot{\theta}_N}\right) = 1 \to \ddot{\theta}_N = 80.1 \to 100$

$\frac{1100}{250}\left(\frac{\dot{\theta}_N}{\ddot{\theta}_N}\right) = 1 \to \dot{\theta}_N = 84.2 \to 100$

$\frac{1562.5}{250}\frac{\theta_N}{\dddot{\theta}_N} = 2 \to \theta_N = 118.3 \to 100$

monotonic I.C.  $=2$    $=1$

$\dddot{x}_\theta + .925\,\ddot{x}_\theta + .880\,\dot{x}_\theta + 1.25\,x_\theta = .740\, U_{-1}(t)$

$\ddot{x}_\theta(0) = -.40, \dot{x}_\theta(0) = +0.825, x_\theta(0) = 0$

$\theta_N = \dot{\theta}_N = \ddot{\theta}_N = 100 \quad \dddot{\theta}_N = 500$

indirect programing

$-\dddot{x} = 0.925\,\ddot{x} + 0.880\,\dot{x} + 1.25\,x - 0.740\, U_{-1}(t)$

# laboratory exercises

The constants of the system are:

$J_1 = 801.14$ lb-ft-sec²/rad
$J_2 = 355.11$ lb-ft-sec²/rad
$B = 1137.98$ lb-ft-sec/rad
$K = 1562.50$ lb-ft/rad
$T_a(t) = 92,500u_{-1}(t)$ lb-ft

RESET Mode disconnect integrator inputs
this can static check

(a) Draw appropriate free body diagrams and use them to write two second-order coupled differential equations in $\theta_1$ and $\theta_2$. Assume zero initial conditions at this point.

(b) Eliminate $\theta_1$ and its derivatives from the two equations and combine them to form one third-order equation in $\theta_2$. Show both the literal and numerical coefficients.

(c) Use the equal coefficient rule discussed in Section 7.2 to estimate maximum absolute values of $\theta_2$ and its derivatives.

(d) Based on the maximums found in part (c), choose a reasonable set of normalizing constants.

(e) Use the normalizing constants chosen in part (d) to magnitude scale

actual max.

$\theta = 90$
$\dot{\theta} = 82$
$\ddot{\theta} = 60$
$\dddot{\theta} = 190$

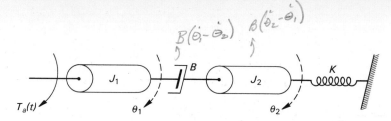

Figure C.1

the equation found in part (b). Assume that the following actual initial conditions apply:

$$\ddot{\theta}_2(0) = -40.0 \text{ rad/sec}^2$$
$$\dot{\theta}_2(0) = +82.5 \text{ rad/sec}$$
$$\theta_2(0) = \quad 0$$

(f) Develop an analog computer flow diagram to solve the scaled equation and initial conditions of part (e). Do not forget the integrator input pots set to the ratio of normalizing constants (see Section 4.1). No time scaling is required.

(g) Calculate a static check for this problem. On the integrator whose output is $-x_\theta$ use a FALSE IC (see Section 5.1) of

$$x_\theta(0) = -0.413$$

(h) Calculate a program check for this problem. Follow Example 5.2.

(i) Patch the flow diagram developed in part (f), perform (confirm) the static check on the computer, and run the problem. Obtain recordings of $\theta_2$ and its derivatives. Read the maximum absolute values off these recordings and compare them with the estimates obtained in part (c). Is rescaling required?

**lab no. 2**
**aerodynamic**
**equation**
**of motion**

An experimental analysis of an aerodynamic system subject to "gust" loading has resulted in the following differential equation:

$$\ddot{z} + 0.1007\dot{z} + 0.5743z = 20te^{-0.3t}$$

The gust forcing function is

$$Ate^{-\alpha t}$$

A function like this has been considered previously, in Example 3.7 and in Problems 3.13 and 4.3.

Assume that the following initial conditions are present:

$$z(0) = 35$$
$$\dot{z}(0) = -20$$

The units are unspecified.

(a) Estimate maximum values for the variables $\ddot{z}$, $\dot{z}$, and $z$. Use the equal coefficient rule or the linear system guidance of Table 7.1. If the coefficient rule is used, recognize that $\ddot{z}_N$ normalizes the forcing function and, because the maximum value of the gust function is known, $\ddot{z}_N$ can be easily chosen. If Table 7.1 is used, superposition applies (if the gust function is replaced by an "equivalent" step function).

(b) Choose a set of normalizing constants based on the above estimates. You should adjust your choice such that a monotonic set is obtained.

(c) Use the normalizing constants chosen above to magnitude scale the system equation and initial conditions, and the differential equation (obtained by implicit programming), from which the forcing function is obtained.

(d) Prepare a complete flow diagram to solve this system.

(e) Prepare static and program checks for this problem. Note that two program checks are really required, one for the system equation and a second for the equation whose solution is the desired gust forcing function.

(f) Patch and run the problem. Record the variable $z$ and its derivatives, and the forcing function.

This problem involves the analysis of two different types of devices which have been proposed for use in starting a small engine. Both devices are designed to produce a high initial starting torque, which is then applied to the engine. The torque produced by one device may be approximated by a rapidly decaying exponential, whereas the second may be described by an impulse forcing function. It has been suggested that the response of the engine to these two different types of applied torques should be very nearly the same. A computer analysis is required in order to investigate system performance.

lab no. 3
engine
starters

The engine dynamics and associated accessory equipment may be represented by the simplified mechanical model shown in Figure C.2. The following constants are known:

$l_1(t) =$ impulsive applied torque $= 36{,}060u_0(t)$ ft-lb
$l_2(t) =$ exponential applied torque $= 78{,}620e^{-218t}$ ft-lb
$K = 6625$ ft-lb/rad
$B = 23.125$ ft-lb-sec/rad
$J = 1.25$ ft-lb-sec²/rad

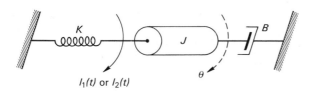

$l_1(t)$ or $l_2(t)$

**Figure C.2**

As defined in Problem 3.4, $u_0(t)$ denotes the unit impulse function. The programming of such a function is explained and illustrated in Example 3.8.

(a) Write the mechanical equation of motion for the engine system in terms of the variable $\theta(t)$.

(b) Use Table 7.1 in the text to estimate maximum values for the problem. To do this, approximate the forcing function with an equivalent step function input. "Worst-case" estimates are desired, such that the same set of normalizing constants can be chosen to scale the equation with either forcing function.

(c) Choose a set of normalizing constants and magnitude scale the system. Assume that the entire system is initially at rest. Select an appropriate time scale factor $n$ if one is required.

(d) Prepare a flow diagram (or diagrams, since there are really two equations to be solved), to mechanize correctly this problem. If the computer available to you has function switches, use them to preclude the necessity of rewiring when solving for the response due to the two different forcing functions.

(e) Patch this problem on the computer and solve for the response due to the inputs $l_1(t)$ and $l_2(t)$. Obtain recordings of angular displacement, velocity, and acceleration versus time for both inputs.

(f) Compare the results obtained and comment on the similarity of the response due to the two different inputs. Can you explain the results quantitatively?

**lab no. 4 radiation equation**

The radiation exhibited by a certain physical system may be described by the following third-order differential equation:

$$\dddot{r} + 6.9\ddot{r} + 80\dot{r} + 400r = 279 \cos\left(t - \tfrac{1}{4}\pi\right)$$

with

$$\ddot{r}(0) = -7.700 \text{ R/sec}^2$$
$$\dot{r}(0) = +2.688 \text{ R/sec}$$
$$r(0) = -1.895 \text{ R}$$

A computer solution of this equation is required. The sinusoidal forcing function generator requires a program as suggested by Problem 3.15.

(a) Use the equal coefficient rule to estimate maximum values for this system. As a starting point, estimate $|\dddot{r}|_{max}$ by using the three initial conditions given and by recognizing the value of the forcing function at $t = 0$.

(b) Based on the above estimates, select a set of normalizing constants. Choose a value for the time scale factor.

(c) Magnitude scale the given equation and initial conditions. Prepare a complete flow diagram and static and program checks.

(d) Run the problem on the computer. Compare the actual maximums with the estimates.

**lab no. 5 nuclear blast overpressure**

The time history of the overpressure caused by the air blast of a nuclear weapon has been given by Brode[1] as:

$$p(t) = P_s(ae^{-\alpha t} + be^{-\beta t} + ce^{-\gamma t})(1 - t)$$

where $t = 0$ corresponds to the instant when the pressure wave, or shock,

[1] Brode, H. L., *A Review of Nuclear Explosion Phenomena Pertinent to Protective Construction*, Report No. R-425-PR, The RAND Corporation, Santa Monica, California (May 1964).

arrives. $P_s$ denotes the maximum overpressure experienced, and is obviously a function of distance from the point of detonation and the size of the blast.

For a point approximately 1500 ft from a 1 megaton surface burst, the maximum overpressure is 1000 psi. The time history of the pressure wave is given by

$$p = 1000(0.15e^{-2.9t} + 0.30e^{-21t} + 0.55e^{-130t})(1 - t)$$

In this equation, $t$ represents a *normalized time* such that the pressure drops to zero when $t = 1$. In actual fact, the duration of the pulse is about 1.20 sec.

(a) Select appropriate magnitude and time scale factors to simulate the pressure wave described above. Note that, in the general formulation

$$a + b + c = 1$$

(b) Prepare an analog computer program to simulate the numerical Brode equation. The multiplication by the linear factor $1 - t$ can be done using the quarter-square multiplier introduced in Problems 8.6, 8.7, and 8.8. Note that, with this device, the output is the negative product of the scaled variables appearing at the $+X$ and $+Y$ inputs.

(c) Run the problem and obtain a recording of $p(t)$ versus time.

This problem involves the selection of a shock absorber for an automobile suspension system. Three shock absorbers are available, where the choice of one is to be based on meeting certain acceleration criteria.

A simplified model of essentially "one corner" of the car is shown in Figure C.3. All motion is assumed to be vertical, and the four individual

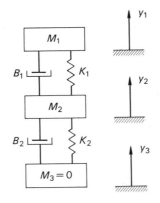

**Figure C.3**

wheel suspension systems are assumed to be identical. The ideal elements and their values are

$M_1$ = mass of one-fourth of auto body = 2.07 lb-sec²/in.
$M_2$ = mass of one wheel, axle, tire, etc. = 0.259 lb-sec²/in.
$M_3$ = "massless" road surface = 0

$K_1$ = stiffness of auto spring = 240 lb/in.
$K_2$ = stiffness of tire = 400 lb/in.
$B_1$ = damping coefficient of shock absorber = variable, to be chosen
$B_2$ = damping coefficient of tire = 4.0 lb-sec/in.

The variables $y_1$, $y_2$, and $y_3$ are measured positive upward from their *reference* or equilibrium, positions. They are defined as

$y_1$ = displacement of auto body
$y_2$ = displacement of axle
$y_3$ = displacement of road surface

This is a *two*-degrees-of-freedom problem, because the shape of the idealized road surface for which the suspension is to be designed (perhaps the test track) is known. The road surface displacement $y_3$ is assumed to be sinusoidal and is described as shown in Figure C.4. The suspension is to be designed for a speed of 60 mph over this surface.

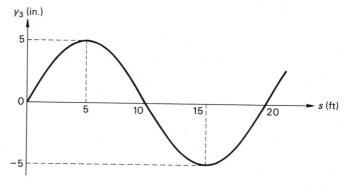

**Figure C.4**

The specifications which the suspension must meet are:

(1)  The maximum vertical acceleration of the car body ($\ddot{y}_1$) must be less than $\pm 3.0$g ($\pm 1160$ in./sec²).
(2)  The maximum vertical acceleration of the wheel-axle assembly ($\ddot{y}_2$) must be less than $\pm 5.0$g ($\pm 1932$ in./sec²). (*Note:* All IC's in this problem are zero, including $\dot{y}_2(0^+)$. However, $\dot{y}_3(0^+) \neq 0$. Energy considerations result in $\ddot{y}_2(0) \neq 0$. Thus, in evaluating the response against the specifications, we ignore the value of $\ddot{y}_2(0)$ and examine $|\ddot{y}_2|_{max}$ for $t > 0$.)

To achieve the design, the following shock absorbers are available:

| *Type:* | Regular | Heavy | Super |
|---|---|---|---|
| $B_1$ (*lb-sec/in.*): | 20 | 40 | 60 |

The equations of motion for the simplified one-wheel automobile suspension system can be solved for the three values of $B_1$ from which the shock absorber is to be chosen. If properly programmed, plots of the auto body and wheel accelerations, $\ddot{y}_1$ and $\ddot{y}_2$, respectively, are readily obtainable. From these, the correct value for $B_1$ can be selected to meet the design criteria.

Since this is a rather complex problem, it should be solved by following these steps:

(a) Use the model of the suspension shown above and write two equations of motion in terms of the assigned variables $y_1$, $y_2$, and $y_3$. (Remember that $y_3$ is really a known "variable.")

(b) Use the sketch of the road surface, shown as a function of *distance s*, to write $y_3(t)$ in the form

$$y_3(t) = A \sin \omega t \text{ in.}$$

Remember that the design speed is 60 mph or 1056 in./sec.

(c) Enter the numerical coefficients in the equations of part (a) and use the equal coefficient rule to estimate maximum values for all the variables. To do this, use a value for $B_1$ of 40 lb-sec/in. (This does not necessarily imply that this is the answer to the design problem!)

(d) Based on the above estimates, select a conservative set of normalizing constants. Based on this choice, and using the results of part (b), select a time scale factor.

(e) Using the normalizing constants selected in part (d), find the magnitude-scaled equations. Assume that all initial conditions associated with $y_1$ and $y_2$ are zero.

(f) Prepare a complete analog computer flow diagram to solve the equations for all three values of $B_1$. This implies that several pots will have different settings for each $B_1$. Do not forget the requirement for integrator input pots.

(g) Calculate a static check for the problem. Since this again requires using some specific value for $B_1$, use 40 lb-sec/in. Also, since all IC's are zero, use the following FALSE IC's:

$$x_1(0) = +0.500 \qquad x_2(0) = -0.200 \qquad x_3(0) = 0$$
$$\dot{x}_1(0) = -0.500 \qquad \dot{x}_2(0) = +0.200$$

(h) Calculate a program check for *each* of the two equations.

(i) Patch the program, confirm the calculated static check values, and run the problem. Remember to remove the FALSE IC's. Check all amplifiers at which overloads could occur and rescale as necessary. Obtain, as a minimum, plots of $\ddot{y}_1$ and $\ddot{y}_2$ versus time for all three shock absorbers.

(j) Note the maximum accelerations obtained using the three different shock absorbers. Compare these maxima with the design criteria and select a value of $B_1$ to meet the design requirements.

In the electrical network shown in Figure C.5, the switch is closed at time $t = 0$. The resistor $R(t)$ represents a nonlinear resistance. The capacitor has been charged to an initial voltage of 45.0 V, where the capacitance $C$ is 0.02 F. The value of inductance $L$ is 0.01 H. At the same time the switch is closed, the resistor is immersed in a liquid nitrogen bath. The initial value of resistance is 0.4 $\Omega$, and $R(t)$ decays exponentially with a time constant $\tau$ of 0.08 sec.

**lab no. 7 nonlinear resistance**

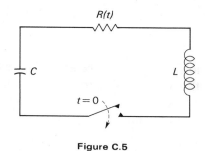

**Figure C.5**

An analog computer study of this circuit is required in terms of the charge $q$ that exists continuously on the capacitor.

(a) Write an expression for $R(t)$ as a function of time.
(b) Write a differential equation in terms of the charge $q$ in the circuit. Put in the numbers.
(c) Determine the minimum and maximum values for the damping ratio $\zeta$ of the circuit.
(d) Use any method available to estimate maximum values for the problem variables. Choose a set of normalizing constants and a time scale factor.
(e) Magnitude scale the equation, develop the flow diagram, and calculate static and program checks. Do not forget the initial condition, and add a FALSE IC on $\dot{q}$ of $+45.0$ A.
(f) Patch and run the problem; record capacitor charge, loop current, and rate of change of current.

**lab no. 8
railroad car**  This problem involves the analysis of a hypothetical railroad car subject to mechanical damping force and spring force constraints. The idealized system is shown in Figure C.6. The railroad car is initially at rest at $z = 0$, where the

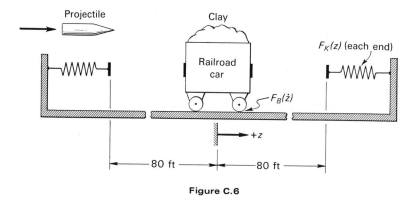

**Figure C.6**

reference direction for $z$ is as shown. At time $t = 0$ a 1-lb projectile traveling to the right at a velocity of 1268 ft/sec strikes, and is captured by, the clay in the car. When this event takes place, 90.31% of the kinetic energy of the projectile is converted to mechanical energy; the remaining 9.69% is lost as

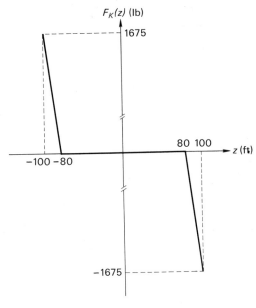

Figure C.7

heat. The total weight of the railroad car and load is 3220 lb. Assume that the length of the small railroad car, relative to the distance between the two springs, is negligible.

The term $F_K(z)$ denotes a linear spring force that is applied anytime for 80 ft $\leq |z| \leq$ 100 ft. The spring constant of each spring is 83.75 lb/ft. In terms of the transfer characteristic notation of Chapter 8, the spring force may be represented as shown in Figure C.7.

The term $F_B(\dot{z})$ denotes a viscous damping force that is equal to $-4\dot{z}$ up to a value of 50 lb, and is constant at $\pm$ 50 lb for any greater velocities. The transfer characteristic is shown in Figure C.8.

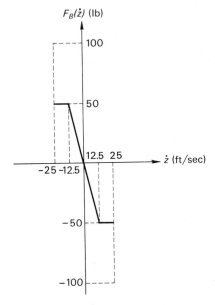

Figure C.8

Since a complete analog computer study of this system is desired, records of $z$, $\dot{z}$, $\ddot{z}$, $F_K(z)$, and $F_B(\dot{z})$ versus time are required. The steps to be followed are:

(a) Normalize the two transfer characteristics (Figures C.7 and C.8) by following the procedure given in Section 8.3. Assume that the maximum values for $F_K$ and $F_B$ are as shown on the sketches; that is, use

$$F_{K_N} = 1675 \text{ lb}$$
$$F_{B_N} = 100 \text{ lb}$$

Sketch the resulting *normalized* transfer characteristics.

(b) Establish the initial value of velocity by using the principle of conservation of energy. Does the result indicate that the sketch of $F_B(\dot{z})$ versus $\dot{z}$ is defined over a sufficient interval on $\dot{z}$?

(c) The differential equation describing this system may be written as

$$M\ddot{z} - F_B(\dot{z}) - F_K(z) = 0$$

The negative signs are due to the way the forces $F_K(z)$ and $F_B(\dot{z})$ are defined. Using the normalizing constants given in part (a), along with

$$z_N = 100 \text{ ft}$$
$$\dot{z}_N = 25 \text{ ft/sec}$$
$$\ddot{z}_N = 25 \text{ ft/sec}^2$$

derive a normalized equation of motion and initial condition. Use the notation

$$x_B(\dot{x}) \triangleq \frac{F_B(\dot{z})}{F_{B_N}}$$

$$x_K(x) \triangleq \frac{F_K(z)}{F_{K_N}}$$

(d) Develop a complete analog computer program to solve this system. Use the precision diode circuits of Appendix B to mechanize the dead space and limiter nonlinearities.

(e) Patch and run the problem. Obtain recordings of $z$, $\dot{z}$, $\ddot{z}$, $F_B(\dot{z})$, and $F_K(z)$ versus time.

**lab no. 9**
**electrical**
**transformer**
**coupling**

This problem involves the computer analysis of a transformer-coupled electrical network, as shown in Figure C.9. The capacitors are initially charged and the switches close at time $t = 0$. The initial currents through the transformer (inductances $L_1$ and $L_2$) are zero. There is mutual inductive coupling $M$ as shown, where

$$M = K\sqrt{L_1 L_2}$$

The reference polarities for the transformer are in accordance with the usual "dot" notation, as shown. The element values are:

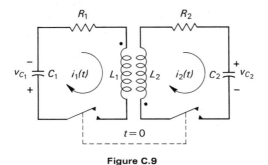

Figure C.9

$$R_1 = 195 \ \Omega \qquad L_1 = 5 \ \text{H} \qquad C_1 = 0.444 \ \mu\text{F} \qquad K = 0.500$$
$$R_2 = 2400 \ \Omega \qquad L_2 = 20 \ \text{H} \qquad C_2 = 2.778 \ \mu\text{F}$$

The initial capacitor voltages are

$$v_{C_1}(0) = -450 \ \text{V} \qquad v_{C_2}(0) = -683.9 \ \text{V}$$

(a) Write two simultaneous second-order differential equations in terms of the charges $q_1$ and $q_2$ in each loop.

(b) Estimate the maximum values for $q_1$ and $q_2$ and their first and second derivatives. To do this, make the simplifying assumption that the equations are "uncoupled," that is, assume two homogeneous second-order equations.

(c) Select a set of normalizing constants, magnitude scale the two coupled equations and initial conditions, and choose a time scale factor.

(d) Prepare a flow diagram, patch the problem, and solve for the currents $i_1$ and $i_2$. How can this be done in terms of the charge? How can a convenient record of capacitor voltages be obtained?

Figure C.10 shows the idealized mechanical model of a real physical system. Assume that the structure supporting spring $K_4$ and the snubber pads is rigid and inextensible. All motion is assumed to take place only in the vertical direction. The reference directions for $y_1$ and $y_2$ as shown are measured from

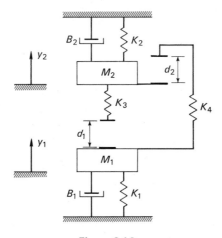

Figure C.10

the equilibrium positions of the two masses. The constants of the system are

$$M_1 = 10.0 \text{ kg} \qquad B_1 = 4.64 \text{ N-sec/m} \qquad K_1 = 542.4 \text{ N/m}$$
$$M_2 = 10.0 \text{ kg} \qquad B_2 = 27.12 \text{ N-sec/m} \qquad K_2 = 154.4 \text{ N/m}$$
$$K_3 = 6666.7 \text{ N/m}$$
$$K_4 = 6666.7 \text{ N/m}$$

$$d_1 = 1.125 \text{ m (at equilibrium)}$$
$$d_2 = 1.125 \text{ m (at equilibrium)}$$

Prior to time $t = 0$, mass $M_2$ is held in place at its equilibrium position while mass $M_1$ is raised a distance of 1.315 m. This means that spring $K_3$ is initially compressed 0.19 m. At time $t = 0$ both masses are released.

(a) Write the two differential equations of motion of this system, using numerical coefficients. There will be some nonlinear force on each mass (equal and opposite) due to the $K_3$–$K_4$ spring system. Do not try to describe this force mathematically but simply include it in each equation as some $F_K(y)$. Write all the initial conditions in the system.

(b) Describe the nonlinear force $F_K(y)$ in terms of a transfer characteristic as defined in Chapter 8. Sketch the transfer characteristic as $F_K(y)$ versus the distance $y_1 - y_2$. Assume that the maximum value of the difference $y_1 - y_2$ is 1.50 m.

(c) Normalize the transfer characteristic by following the procedure of Section 8.3. Choose some $F_{K_N}$ of 2500 N and assume $(y_1 - y_2)_N$ is 1.50 m.

(d) Use the following normalizing constants to magnitude scale the equations and initial condition of part (a):

$$\ddot{y}_{N_1} = 200 \text{ m/sec}^2 \qquad \ddot{y}_{N_2} = 200 \text{ m/sec}^2$$
$$\dot{y}_{N_1} = 10 \text{ m/sec} \qquad \dot{y}_{N_2} = 10 \text{ m/sec}$$
$$y_{N_1} = 1.50 \text{ m} \qquad y_{N_2} = 1.50 \text{ m}$$

Choose a time scale factor.

(e) Prepare a complete flow diagram to solve this system. Use the precision dead-zone circuit from Appendix B to generate the nonlinear spring force term.

(f) Run the problem and solve for $y_1$ and $y_2$ and their derivatives. Also record $F_K(y)$.

# bibliography

(1)  Ashley, J. R. *Introduction to Analog Computation* (New York: John Wiley & Sons, Inc., 1963).

(2)  Cheng, D. K. *Analysis of Linear Systems* (Reading, Mass.: Addison-Wesley Publishing Co., Inc., 1959).

(3)  Cowan, J. D., and H. S. Kirschbaum. *Introduction to Circuit Analysis* (Columbus, Ohio: Charles E. Merrill Books, Inc., 1961).

(4)  Craig, E. J. *Laplace and Fourier Transforms for Electrical Engineers* (New York: Holt, Rinehart and Winston, 1964).

(5)  D'Azzo, J. J., and C. H. Houpis. *Control System Analysis and Synthesis* (New York: McGraw-Hill Book Company, Inc., 1960).

(6)  Forrest, J. "Simulating High-Order Algebraic Equations with Linear Analog Computer Elements." *Instruments and Control Systems*, Vol. 38, No. 3 (March, 1965), 162–64.

(7)  Goldberg, J. H. *Automatic Controls: Principles of Systems Dynamics* (Boston: Allyn and Bacon, Inc., 1964).

(8)  Howe, R. M. *Design Fundamentals of Analog Computer Components* (Princeton, N.J.: D. Van Nostrand Co., Inc., 1960).

(9)  Jackson, A. S. *Analog Computation* (New York: McGraw-Hill Book Company, Inc., 1960).

(10)  James, M. L., G. M. Smith, and J. C. Wolford. *Analog and Digital Computer Methods in Engineering Analysis* (Scranton, Penn.: International Textbook Co., 1965).

(11)  Johnson, C. L. *Analog Computer Techniques* (New York: McGraw-Hill Book Company, Inc., 1956).

(12)  Langill, A. W., Jr. *Automatic Control Systems Engineering* (Englewood Cliffs, N.J.: Prentice-Hall, Inc., 1965).

(13)  Pennington, R. H. *Introductory Computer Methods and Numerical Analysis* (New York: The Macmillan Company, 1965).

(14)  Rogers, A. E., and T. W. Connolly. *Analog Computation in Engineering Design* (New York: McGraw-Hill Book Company, Inc., 1960).

(15)  Truitt, T. D., and A. E. Rogers. *Basics of Analog Computers* (New York: John F. Rider, Inc., 1960).

# answers to

1.6(a). Order 1, degree 2

1.6(c). Order 2, degree 1

1.7(b). Linear, variable coefficient, nonhomogeneous

1.7(d). Nonlinear, variable coefficient, homogeneous

1.9. $\omega_n = 3$ rad/sec, critical damping $\zeta = 1$

2.1. $K = 0.4651$

2.3.

2.6(b). $x_o = 0.250x_1 - 0.100x_2$

2.7. Gain $= 2$

2.9(a). $\dot{x} + 2x = 0$

3.2.

# selected problems

3.4. $\dfrac{d}{dt}u_{-2}(t) = u_{-1}(t)$ or $s\left(\dfrac{1}{s^2}\right) = s\,;\dfrac{d}{dt}u_{-1}(t) = u_0(t)$ or $s\left(\dfrac{1}{s}\right) = 1$

3.8.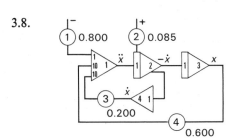

3.11. $z = (10by - x)/(1 + 5a)$

3.13. $\ddot{x}_f + 2\alpha\dot{x}_f + \alpha^2 x_f = 0$
$\dot{x}_f(0) = A$
$x_f(0) = 0$

3.15.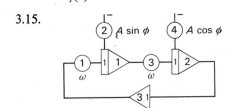

Both IC's negative for $A$ positive and $\phi$ in first quadrant. Outputs are

A1 $= +A \sin(\omega t + \phi)$
A2 $= +A \cos(\omega t + \phi)$
A3 $= -A \cos(\omega t + \phi)$

4.1(c). Conditionally stable: $(s^2 + 2)(s^3 + s^2 + 2s + 1)$

4.3. $|\dot{x}_f|_{max} = A$, and it occurs at $t = 0$

4.6. $\ddot{x}_y + 0.600\dot{x}_y + 0.900x_y = 0.720u_{-1}(t)$
Nonzero IC's would also have to be scaled.

4.8. $\dddot{x}_\theta + 0.925\ddot{x}_\theta + 0.880\dot{x}_\theta + 1.25x_\theta = 0.740u_{-1}(t)$
$\ddot{x}_\theta(0) = -0.400$
$\dot{x}_\theta(0) = 0.825$
$x_\theta(0) = 0$

4.10(b). $\dot{x}_v + 0.667x_v = \sin t$

5.4(a). $x_f = -0.629e^{-2.18t}$

5.4(b). Both are FALSE, as indicated by dotted lines.
$\dot{x}(0) = 0.288$
$x(0) = 0.843$

5.4(c). A2 output is $+0.129$

5.5. A2 output would become $+1.149$; this is invalid since it indicates a slight overload at $t = 0$.

6.1(a). $\zeta = 0.5$,   $\omega_n = 10^5$ rad/sec

6.1(c). $\omega_d = 86,600$ rad/sec;   choose $n = 100,000$

6.5(a). $z_N = 2.5$,   $\dot{z}_N = 10$,   $\ddot{z}_N = 100$

6.5(b). P2 $= 10$,   P4 $= 4$

6.8(a). Choose $y_N = A\tau$ and $\dot{y}_N = A$; pot setting is then $1/\tau$

6.9(a). $\dot{\omega} + 14.3\omega = 8980u_{-1}(t)$

7.2. $|\dddot{\theta}|_{max} = 370$ rad/sec³
$|\ddot{\theta}|_{max} = 80.1$ rad/sec²
$|\dot{\theta}|_{max} = 84.2$ rad/sec
$|\theta|_{max} = 118.3$ rad

7.5. $\ddot{q} + 50\dot{q} + 100,000q = 10,000u_{-1}(t)$
$|\ddot{q}|_{max} = 10^4$ A/sec
$|\dot{q}|_{max} = 200$ A
$|q|_{max} = 0.2$ C

7.8. Use superposition, due to step plus IC.
$|\ddot{y}|_{max} = 25 + 50$
$|\dot{y}|_{max} = 5 + 10$
$|y|_{max} = 2 + 2$

7.9. $M = |G(j\omega)| = 2.54/400 = |y|_{max}/200$
$|y|_{max} = 1.27$
$|\dot{y}|_{max} = 63.5$
$|\ddot{y}|_{max} = 508$

8.2.

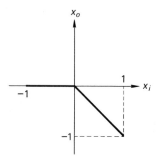

8.7.    $x_w = w/w_N$, where $w_N = u_N v_N$

8.8.    One possible arrangement is shown below. The pot settings shown are for the equation

$$\ddot{x} + 0.2\dot{x} + x = 0.45 u_{-1}(t)$$

where

$$\zeta = 0.1, \quad \omega_n = 1 \text{ rad/sec}, \quad \text{and} \quad A = 0.45$$

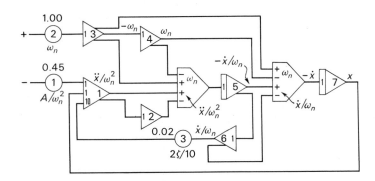

8.9(b).

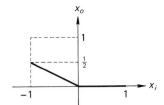

8.10.    Choose

$$y_N = 20, \quad \dot{y}_N = 40{,}000, \quad \text{and} \quad n = 2000$$

The equation is

$$\dot{x} + x|x| = 0$$
$$x(0) = 0.900$$

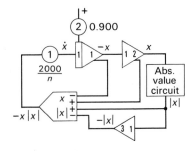

**9.2.** $\quad G(s) = \dfrac{1/M}{s^2 + (B/M)s + (K/M)}$

**9.4.** $\quad G(s) = \dfrac{1}{(J_1 J_2/B)s^3 + (J_1 + J_2)s^2 + (J_1 K/B)s + K}$

**9.8(a).** $\quad G(s) = s/(s + 1/RC)$

**9.8(c).** $\quad x_2/x_1 = s/(s + 20)$

**9.10.** $\quad G(s) = (Z/F)(Y/Z)$, where $(Z/F) = \frac{1}{2}$
$\quad -sY = (-1/s)[(-1/s)(25Y - Z) + (0.2Z - 27Y)] + (3Y - Z)$

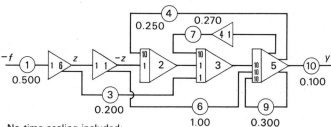

No time scaling included;
$n \cong 10$ required

**10.4.** Choose $s_N = 75$

$$Q(0) = 12{,}500 \quad \text{and} \quad Q(75) \cong 8 \times 10^7$$

Choose $Q_N = 10^8$

**10.5.** P6 (only) would change to 0.672

**11.5.** From a Bode plot:

$$M_{db} = \quad -1 \quad \text{dB for } \omega = \quad 10 \text{ rad/sec}$$
$$M_{db} = \quad -7.2 \text{ dB for } \omega = 150 \text{ rad/sec}$$
$$M_{db} = -18.3 \text{ dB for } \omega = 377 \text{ rad/sec}$$

**11.7(a).** $\quad e_a = Ri_a + L\dfrac{di_a}{dt} + K_g\dot{\theta}$

$\quad K_T i_a = J\ddot{\theta} + B\dot{\theta}$

**11.7(b).** $\quad \dot{x}_1 = x_2$
$\quad \dot{x}_2 = (K_T/J)x_3 - (B/J)x_2$
$\quad \dot{x}_3 = (1/L)e_a - (R/L)x_3 - (K_g/L)x_2$

**11.7(c).** State variable equations are *not* a function of $x_1$ because, without a rotary spring, there is no potential energy storage. Hence, choose *two* state variables, $\theta$ and $i_a$.

**11.10.** $\quad \dddot{y} + 6\ddot{y} + 11\dot{y} + 6y = 2\dot{u} + 3u$

# index

1
2
3
4
5
6
7
8

**index**